More Than A Midwife

Stories of Glory, Grace, and Motherhood

More Than A Midwife

Stories of Glory, Grace, and Motherhood

Mary Sommers

MAVEN
MARK
BOOKS

MavenMark Books, an imprint of HenschelHAUS Publishing, Inc.
Milwaukee, Wisconsin

Published by
MavenMark Books
(a division of HenschelHAUS Publishing, Inc.)
2625 S. Greeley St. Suite 201
Milwaukee, WI 53207
www.henschelHAUSbooks.com

Please contact the publisher for quantity discounts.

ISBN: 978-1-59598-106-6 (paperback)
ISBN: 978-1-59598-149-3 (Kindle)

LCCN: 2011942021

Library of Congress Cataloging-in-Publication information available on request.

Photo credits:
Front cover: Leah Wolf and Judith Halek
Back cover: Melanie Wolf (with author holding son Julian)

Printed in the United States of America.

Dedicated to mothers, midwives, and doulas the world over.

Acknowledgments

My heartfelt gratitude to my sister midwives, colleagues, and friends who have supported and guided me along my journey.

… to all the mothers and families I've had the honor to assist over the years;

… special thanks to Suzanne Clores, my writing mentor;

… and to my family—my parents, my husband Michael White, and our five children: Hannah, Erin, Jordan, Greta, and Natalia.

—Mary Sommers

Introduction

Childbirth is raw, messy, sometimes sensual, sometimes hard. It is not, by any means, a passive medical procedure. By its very nature, childbirth mingles the power of life with fear, making it easy for the general public to get a negative perception of what is essentially a transformative event. This book is a collection of women's stories I've gathered after working for 25 years as a community midwife. In offering an intimate, alternative look at birth, I hope to encourage a fundamental change in women's attitudes towards this opportunity for personal and spiritual transformation.

My perspective on childbirth comes from being a World Health Fellow, a Certified Professional Midwife, a Director of Nurse-Midwifery Services at several community health centers, and the International Board for CASA, the first professional midwifery school in Mexico. I am involved in global midwifery projects including a project in Malawi, Africa, and a community midwife working on home births, birth center births, and hospital doula births throughout the American Midwest. From all of my fieldwork and involvement in the lives of pregnant women around the world, I have come to realize the following. The process of birth is the process of life itself, rich and complex and deserving of our full participation. To desire only the elusive, pain-free or easy birth is to miss the point, I now tell so many of my patients. Though such a claim is sometimes lost on them at first, they eventually come to understand, as I did, once they deliver. Birth is so much more than an external event placed on us to "get through." In fact, it is a very real—perhaps the most real—moment in a mother's life that exposes us to who we are and who we are to become, both as mothers and as women.

Midwifery showed itself to me as a spiritual act of service. Back in 1966, I was six years old and sitting in the front row of folding chairs in our church basement, clutching my red Kool-Aid and eager to hear of the unique travels of Sr. Anne Cauzillo, a missionary nun from Ghana visiting our parish in Detroit, Michigan. Sr. Anne shared stories of her work as both a midwife and a nurse at a leprosy clinic. I was transfixed. I imagined myself like her—in a faraway land, mature, capable, and involved in something greater than myself. A path like Sr. Anne's seemed to answer my prayers, but for one exception: I had a strong desire to be a mother, not a nun. Nevertheless, I knew I had had a brush with my life's purpose.

I started educating others about birth shortly afterward. I am the fourth of thirteen children, and since my mother was pregnant most of my childhood, I had plenty of opportunities to ask questions about her expanding belly. To me, babies were the best. I once confessed to my mother that I hoped to have 36 children. She smiled and in mock surprise assured me that maybe my expectations were a bit high. Her words did not discourage me. I remember setting aside 36 names for my future children.

When I inquired to my pregnant mother about "how babies were born," she carefully replied, "with a special secret." This reply was far more fascinating, and far less disappointing, than her responses to whether or not Santa Claus or the Easter Bunny was real. My mother was practical and had little patience for mystery, but when she revealed that women have a very special opening that allows a baby to pass through, I was mystified. Imagine that, *a special hole*. Babies knew when it was time to begin their journey through this special hole *right on their birthdays*.

She cautioned me not to tell everyone, especially my best friend Michelle, whose parents were not ready to share this secret with her. Well, I have always believed education should be free and available to all who would listen. I would have no part of keeping this miraculous news to myself. I immediately shared the news with Michelle and my sisters, and skipped down the street shouting out the wonders of women's bodies. I was not to be stopped. Girls everywhere, I thought, should know about childbirth.

While my education in the birth process was a public education experience, my introduction to the Divine Feminine was a Catholic experience. In some families, First Communion was a catechism event, but in my family, it was also a sacred ritual. I would receive my First Communion at the regular Sunday liturgy with my entire family, plus cousins, uncles, aunts, godparents, and grandmother in attendance. The preparation for this event began with acquiring the white garb—a white dress that had once belonged to my cousin and was previously worn by my three eldest sisters. New black shoes and white socks and gloves were purchased, and of course, a veil. On the First Communion day, I would merit special attention and congratulations from my parents. It would be one of the few days we would eat out at a restaurant for Sunday brunch.

We also visited the local Christian store. My grandmother and mother both displayed several images of patron saints around our home. St. Jude, St. Joseph, Mary, and Christ statues were on every shelf. In the weeks before my Communion, it was time to select my very own statue of Mary—one that would represent my special relationship with my patron saint. The store was thick with Catholic symbols: crosses, crucifixes, and stained glass of biblical scenes. I had never seen so many different statues of Mary. There were tender-looking Marys with their head bowed to the side, soft images of young girls with porcelain skin. A few of them appeared to be anemic. They looked sweet and serene, but not up to the divine task. The Mary in my mind was a mother, *the* Mother.

My eyes scanned the store until my eyes fell upon a statue of Mary that struck me at my core. This Mary had a larger build than most the other Marys. She had strong, almost exaggerated features, darker skin, and a Roman nose. I remember distinctly how compelled I was by her giant bare feet and the snake beneath them. She was not avoiding or frightened by the snake, but quite confidently holding it down with power. This precious image represented everything I believed Mary to be. Inspiring and inspired, protector of the vulnerable, poised in the face of grief, anguish and judgment. The feminine redeemed through the power of motherhood.

Much to my grandmother and mother's distress, we brought the statue home and placed it in my room that day.

That statue would adorn our family alter every year during May, and eventually, my mother grew fond of it. She knew from experience what it meant to be strong and feminine. The image became a symbol of other things, too, over the years. Intimacy. Labor. Once it fell and broke in half, but I successfully glued "my" Mary together. Resilience. She followed me through many moves and many apartments. Loyalty. Commitment.

I carried her lessons, and relearned them again and again over the decades of practicing midwifery. The women in this book—the adolescent mothers, the clinically depressed ones, the eccentric and privileged and grief-stricken and impoverished ones—all embody the teachings of this particular Mary by the time they bear their children. They stand poised and strong; they crush the snake for the sake of their own vulnerability and the vulnerability of their children. They thrive.

Thanks to the families I have served, I have had over a thousand opportunities to learn the meaning of birth and life, and the divine power of motherhood. This book is their stories.

Eve

ight weeks before her second child was to be born, Eve took my natural childbirth class. After the first session, she and her husband, Adam, remained after everyone else had left. She sat plumply, her prominent belly rolled onto her lap as if holding court. I could tell she wanted to talk, partly from the self-deprecating jokes about how "ignorant" she'd been the last time she was pregnant (her harrowing first birth had ended in an emotionally stressful Caesarean section), and partly because of her overly confident vows that "this time would be different" and that she would "do it right." Adam nodded almost robotically. The two of them exuded insecurity.

Over mugs of chamomile tea, I listened to Eve's host of current complaints, all of which she blamed on the Caesarean delivery nearly three years ago: chronic back pain and a lack of sexual arousal and interest, feelings of isolation from her partner, and many months of disconnection from her infant. My eyes went to Adam, who seemed distant and uninterested in his wife's litany of complaints. He hardly appeared to listen as Eve retold the events of her birth.

"I'm still confused about what happened," she said, as if other people were to blame.

She had chosen the best hospital—a popular medical center in Chicago—known for its modern obstetrics and fashionable delivery rooms with gorgeous views of Lake Michigan. Among the amenities were marble floors, cherry beds, spacious rooms, and a hospital menu that included steaks and champagne. She was 40 weeks pregnant when her provider offered to induce her labor. While it's not best practice, some upscale hospitals do offer scheduled inductions for convenience—a seductive offer for any bloated, exhausted mother-to-be. Eve had infinite trust in her provider, a physician not much older than herself, friendly and educated at the best universities. He was efficient and thorough in his practice of medicine. When he offered a series of options for induction, he cautioned that there was some risk to the event, but that the risk was small. She didn't ask for more detail.

As the provider suspected, the offer appealed to Eve. She was anxious to have her baby and the timing seemed right for other reasons—though they had nothing to do with her infant. The nursery was complete, her mother could come in from California to assist her after birth, Adam's travel schedule had stabilized. It was a quick and easy decision: she agreed.

She went to the induction excited and optimistic. She had called her family, who placed their bets on the exact hour of delivery. She brought a CD player and some videos to the hospital to distract her from the long wait. She entered her labor room at 9 o'clock that morning. A resident applied a prostaglandin gel to her cervix in hopes of prepping the cervix for more intense contractions and then, at 11 a.m., she was given an IV with Pitocin, a synthetic version of the hormone oxytocin which, when released during labor, causes the contractions of the uterus. Soon came strong contractions. She requested an epidural. She was four centimeters dilated and elated. She anticipated the birth of her baby by five that evening. She and her husband popped in a video and waited.

To look at Eve's pregnancy from the standpoint of traditional Western medicine, she did everything right. She accepted every screen for every possible genetic defect. Her child had none. She rejoiced at the image of her son on the ultrasound, and delighted when she was told there was no reason for him not to be bright and beautiful. At the prime birthing age of 30, she had a good career and a sense of entitlement. She felt sure her wishes for a good birth and a brilliant baby would "come true."

She had taken the hospital childbirth preparation course, taught by an enthusiastic instructor who had mentioned induction was one of many choices women had available to them for their delivery. Additional choices included epidural anesthesia and a Caesarean section if they desired to avoid labor all together. While the instructor did offer that birth could be positive—and had herself had a positive birth experience—she cautioned the women not to be unrealistic about their expectations. Birth has always been hard and painful, she said, and it was a mistake to think your birth would be any different without some basic interventions.

The hospital, she went on to say, would allow them to have an epidural as soon as they arrived if they needed it. "But you won't be in labor more than 14 hours," she assured. The day-long course had shown a few birth videos, mostly of smiling couples looking pain-free and happy with their newborns. Eve left feeling satisfied and relieved with the information provided. She found the class's descriptions of birth agreeable and in line with her hopes for her own birth. There were no techniques to remember; her physicians were capable of starting her labor for her, controlling her pain, and, ultimately, handling her baby's entry into the world. There was nothing for her to do.

As I listened to Eve's story, I noticed she possessed only a portion of the knowledge women need before entering childbirth. She said nothing about a birth plan, about the role of her partner Adam, or how she would cope with complications. I wondered if Eve purposely avoided finding out more for the sake of simplicity. She had, in fact, made one lone inquiry about a natural childbirth—inspired to do so after reading an article. But the provider responded with confusion; why would she want to endure pain? There are a few "superwomen" who can endure labor, he continued, but "going granola" was neither his recommendation nor his preference. Eve had already begun to back down when he reiterated how he wanted her to be realistic about birth and to be "open" to all of her options. She acquiesced, subverting her deeper desire to ask questions in order to protect her present understanding of the birth process.

There's a famous proverb I heard once listening to a tape by Jungian psychologist Clarissa Pinkola Estes about the desire to break out of the mouse-trap of ignorance. To paraphrase: "Women are like mice in the traps; they are only aware that they are in the trap when the cheese is gone." Eve fell into the behavior that Dr. Estes says is so common for women who are "happy to keep eating the cheese." She accepted the information given to her as if it were all she had to know. She behaved as if birth was an ordinary event that happened within prescribed parameters. She felt safe. Many of her friends had delivered at the same hospital—even with her same provider. In short, she was happy to keep eating the cheese.

Her memory of the next series of events is vague: first, her uterus became hyper-stimulated from the effects of the Pitocin. This was one of the possible risks of induction, one that Eve never imagined would apply to her (and that she never even inquired about). The supply of blood and oxygen to the fetus slowed. As hospital staff rushed in to turn down the Piticion level, the baby's heartbeat dipped on the monitor. Eve began to panic: this was not what she had planned—or what she even considered to be within the realm of possibility. The instructor in the birth class never made mention of abnormal heartbeats. She started to hyperventilate.

Nurses offered oxygen and suggested she lie on her side. She accepted and obeyed but, although her baby's heart beat began to recover, her panic continued. She had received an epidural, but did not realize what an epidural did—it immobilized her lower body. She could not follow her impulse to leave, to run, or to stop the process even if she wanted to. Her panic increased and she remained in a heightened state.

While she described the incident to me, Adam sat as if listening, but his face was vacant. At the time of the event, I learned later, he had behaved like an interpreter. He explained her hysteria to the staff in hope of a remedy—any remedy—that would save her. Her provider offered a Caesarean section: Adam and Eve took it. He was relieved. His doubts that Eve ever possessed the stamina for birth were confirmed, and they were getting help. Their decision felt right.

An anesthesia drape was placed just below her neck. Waves of panic washed over her. An oxygen mask covered her mouth. She stared upward at the ceiling, breathing deeply and worrying that the anesthesia would not have a lasting effect. Masked individuals moved around her, engaged in their medical duties. She lay on the table while her provider presided over the activities beyond the drape. Her legs were like stone, the numbness crept up to her abdomen and then toward her chest. Though she had little sensation in her body, she felt her heart beating, and became acutely aware of her material surroundings. She was the observer of her own body, a mere spectator at this extraordinary event.

Adam was seated next to her, wearing a blue scrub suit and cap. She didn't feel the incision into the skin or the retraction of layers beneath the skin, the layers of subcutaneous fat, the fascia, the abdominal muscles, nor the thin membrane protecting the abdominal cavity. The doctor cut another incision once he reached the uterus. This incision he cut side to side about three inches in length. There was an opening, a small amount of amniotic fluid leaked out, and he suctioned it. Shortly after, she felt a tug and someone exerting pressure on the top of the uterus. It was not painful, and within a few seconds, her healthy, eight-pound son was shown to her.

She lay on the operating table, delighted yet confused. Why hadn't the birth been "normal"? Why had things gone wrong when doctors were in charge of the whole process? She felt disappointed and nearly victimized, but in order to protect her fragile mental state, she began to rationalize. Birth is all the same, she convinced herself, whether C-section or vaginal: it was just a different opening. The important thing was she had a healthy child. But then why should she feel disappointed? The wave of panic began to rise and crest. Before it had a chance to crash, the sound of her crying, healthy baby snapped her out of it. The role of motherhood took over.

As she told me the birth story, she mentioned that she still has a peculiar sense of fear. Some of the more the frightening memories have faded, but other parts still remained a total blank. She has spent hours trying to make sense of what had happened, specifically, why, when she thinks about her birth, she feels naked and vulnerable. Why she has the distinct feeling of having missed something.

Her current pregnancy made her worry about her mental and physical well-being. The impact of another difficult postpartum adjustment would devastate her marriage and her mothering. Though she had committed to the idea of a natural childbirth this time around—even joined Caesarean prevention groups and read blogs about women's options post-C-section—she was still filled with regret about her previous choices.

It's not my belief that women are at fault for the outcome of their problematic births. But women like Eve can't abandon responsibility and then blame the "system" for ruining their birth experience. Helping Eve understand this truth about herself would be challenging; she was defensive, stubborn, and argumentative. But I was hopeful she had the ability to overcome her anxiety and take responsibility for the birth of her next child.

I continued to work with the couple for the duration of my class. One way in which I get to know couples is I have them reflect on past experiences in which they felt successful or unsuccessful. They can compare each experience to gain insight, to see how they operate in the world and in defining moments. Since the feelings of strength and disappointment are both visceral, they are therefore memorable, particularly during challenges such as birthing a child when instinct kicks in. I learned a lot about Adam and Eve during this process of reflection.

Running marathons was among Eve's successes—a difficult feat that takes preparation and stamina. She was proud of her qualities and seemed aware that she possessed an extraordinary physical ability. An experience in which she felt unsuccessful, however, involved a trip to Alaska to join a friend to climb Denali. She arrived only to discover she did not have the right hiking boots. As they started up the mountain, she panicked, blaming her panic on the poor fit of the boots she had. She descended and spent the entire trip waiting for her friends to return. It seemed like the predictability of running a marathon comforted her, despite the hard work, while lack of preparedness and unfulfilled expectations made her panic. It was why she and Adam made such a great team. Adam's greatest success was driving a military vehicle through enemy territory when his fellow soldier lost control and "freaked out." He stayed steady in times of panic. As a former army officer, he was accustomed to handling non-standard procedures with calm and control. He knew how to follow rules, and his deep respect for hierarchy kept him from questioning authority. The emotional disconnect I saw in him with regard to Eve, however, was the downside of such controlled behavior.

The couple seemed to understand their successes and difficulties once we spoke about them. I learned a lot from Adams's stiff body language and pleading eyes. He hoped I had an answer on how best to help Eve. At the time, the best I could do was to hand them a few names of sympathetic nurse-midwives and physicians, for which they were grateful.

The meeting with the first provider did not go well. Eve admitted to having a break-down in the waiting area. The front office reminded her of the office of her former obstetrician, and she started hyperventilating. When they finally met with the provider, the provider insisted that she receive continuous fetal monitoring during the labor. Eve would have no part of it. She began to cry then —and again when retelling me the story, her hand in fists, hopeless and raging at the system, "Why is it so difficult for me to find someone to let me have a vaginal birth?"

In a later conversation I had with this provider, she confided in me, "Eve is a lawsuit waiting to happen."

Other meetings went similarly. For Eve to get the right provider, she was going to have to do her homework and keep a good attitude. Her pregnancy continued on course, but Eve became increasingly adamant, frustrating her providers by demanding that they change their protocols to meet her needs. She kept changing doctors in search of one who would comply with her requests; she didn't want continual fetal monitoring, didn't want an I.V. She went through a number of providers. A few doubted her ability to be realistic about birth, a few suggested she take medication for her anxiety disorder, a few suggested she just have a another C-section. Many thought she was a nut case.

Though I had recommended the most progressive providers I knew, none seemed excited to take on Eve. Fortunately, I was finally able to connect the couple with a nurse-midwife, one who specifically assisted women desiring a natural birth after a Caesarean birth. Glenda, the midwife, was unfazed by Eve's panic attacks. She enjoyed guiding couples through the birth process. She met with the couple often, offered Eve a pain management plan that included a soaking in a tub, warm clothes for her lower belly, massage, and the continuous presence of a midwife.

Initially, Eve bristled at the thought of signing the informed consent documents required by the hospital. She felt the documents were scare tactics. She had to sign waivers against continuous monitoring, something she also hesitated to sign. Each step gave Eve more responsibility for her decisions. Each step gave Adam the opportunity to take responsibility for being more present in Eve's upcoming birth, from being passive to being a participant—equal with Eve and her provider.

I also agreed to be Eve's labor coach. She had many hurdles to overcome if she was to recover from the trauma of her last birth and not repeat the same mistakes, and I took pains to let her know. Her lack of research into other birth options was akin to not preparing herself to hike Denali. Her faith in the provider's promise that birth would be "normal" resembled her assumption that chasing a boyfriend to an out-of-state college would work out. She was not prepared for variations of normal in any of these situations. When the pressure was on, she abandoned the power to decide her fate. Rather than directing her child's delivery, she panicked, and had held her provider responsible for the choices she made under duress.

In a series of private sessions before the birth, I had the couple reflect on their prior life experiences and recall times when each of them felt they had found strength in themselves and in each other. I also challenged them to remember events in which they gave into feelings of weakness and did not challenge themselves. Through this work, Adam and Eve were able to articulate what they had lost when they did not challenge themselves, and what they had accomplished when they felt courageous. We set about creating a birth plan that did not convey an "ideal birth," but did set forth virtues they wished to strive for during the upcoming birth. These virtues included ways they could both express courage, grace, love, truth, and honesty.

Eve was drawn to Adam because of his static, steady presence in other matters. He was a good provider, not prone to hysteria, and seemed capable of providing for her the outside comfort of a good life style. He is fundamentally passive. She, on the contrary, is full of energy and I saw how he might be drawn to her potential to lead him from his more bland, mundane routine to one that might promise excitement and color. They were a powerful match, but each needed a fundamental change in the approach not only to birth, but to life. Eve was used to relying on others to make decisions for her, and needed to step into the decision-making role herself. Adam needed to protect her from harm, but not rescue her from it.

I increasingly enjoyed my private sessions with the couple. Eve's sharp distrust of medicine and its false promises for painless birth faded over time. She began to trust herself. She looked forward to her birth, and accepted her past birth experience as part of her life experience. She saw the "failure" of a promise an important part of Adam's and her journey. The couple now desired a birth that allowed them to explore their authentic selves without fear of humiliation, disappointment, or shame. She was free to panic, and knew this time neither she, nor Adam, nor her midwife would succumb to the fear of her behavior. They would celebrate her humanness. They would allow her to find herself in the process. Eve was no longer afraid of being vulnerable and Adam was not afraid of her vulnerability.

Her contractions began on a Sunday morning. She lay across her bed with a warm cloth against her lower belly. Adam lay next to her. I arrived at her home in hopes of giving her labor support and delaying the trip to the hospital in order to allow her to labor mostly at home. With each contraction, she squeezed Adam's hand, moaned, and moved further into her journey.

We arrived at the hospital when she was approaching hard labor. The wave of panic rose. Instead of fearing its power and height, she dove deep inside, moving past difficulties she had carried with her throughout her life: betrayals, losses, fears. She could feel her knees go weak. Adam and Glenda held her up. She could hear every sound in the room, feel the presence of all three of us, but also entered the trance-like state in which many women find themselves during active labor. It is a highly sensitive, deeply intuitive state. It is a state in which Eve, historically, had always feared going.

As the contractions grew stronger, she closed her eyes and plunged into darkness. She could feel every movement of the baby, even feel his imminent arrival, yet still she combated hissing voices of doubt. She retched. She needed a guardian angel to help her defeat the demons, to keep her from falling into the pit of anxiety. She retched again, shaking her head as if shaking snakes out of her hair. And then, by some miracle, came the ancient knowledge and awareness she needed. When Glenda reminded her that she had ample room in her pelvis for the baby to fit through, Eve believed her.

Joy overcame her fear as she pursued the extraordinary task. She sought solitude during the contractions. Sometimes she would weep, sometimes she felt inexplicable joy, and sometimes she could not restrain herself and would howl using the full strength of her voice. The serious mission of birthing human life onto this planet had become clear to her. Her ability to control and have access to parts of herself that had always lain dormant amazed her, as did their odd familiarity. Outside she shuddered, wept, and clung on to Adam with each contraction, but inside she felt pure delight.

One of the roles of midwives is to support women while they explore their inner depths during childbirth. Years of midwifery have taught me to allow women to feel their vulnerabilities, without rescuing them and without abandoning them. Birth is complex; the spiritual components of birth are hidden from ordinary reality.

As Eve climbed the mountain, this time with poorly fitting shoes and all, she felt the sensation of crawling up a steep mountain, wet rocks, sliding hands and hazardous cliffs from which she could fall. She held on to our hands, leaned against our bodies, and finally crawled to the mountain top. When we pointed to the head of the baby emerging, she felt anxious, her heart started beating faster, and yet with each push, she felt her second son squeeze himself through. She reached down with her arms to greet him as he erupted from her vagina. It was a perfect moment in time. The birth team embraced her in a circle, and she spoke through tears of joy: "I did it," she said, "I did it."

The Woman Who was Bound
Becomes Free

I met Jan about twenty years ago during the sixth month of her pregnancy. At the time, low-income mothers without insurance had few options for labor and delivery. These women had to either pay out of pocket or deliver at the county hospital, which at the time offered no private rooms, leaving women to labor side by side, factory style. The labor unit at the county hospital was referred to as the "labor line." Jan was 21 when she found herself unexpectedly pregnant. It was a difficult time in her life to have a child. She was an art student, waiting tables on weekends, and miles away from her family.

She had an unusual look for those times, full of contradictions. She felt drawn to all things black, and yet her style of dress was feminine and frilly. Her style sought neither harmony nor provocation. She fancied tattoos ten years before they become fashionable, yet her tattoos were statements of peace rather than rebellion. On each upper arm were quotes by Gandhi. She flaunted her indifference; she identified herself as "punk," but only her white, closely cropped hair looked punk; her attire was often conventional. She identified, somewhat, with her generation's attitude of contempt, though contempt for what was unclear.

She had an on-off relationship with the father of the baby. He was not entirely invested in being the father of her child despite their living together for most of the pregnancy. He had an addiction to alcohol and cigarettes. Jan detested both. She was a vegetarian, and had conscientiously downed at least eight glasses of water a day. She wanted to avoid having to give birth at the county hospital so she sought a home birth.

She was referred to us by her midwife at the county hospital. She had discussed with her midwife a desire to give birth naturally and in her home. She thought that she could not afford a home birth due to her limited income and her often unemployed boyfriend. Her midwife informed her that Val, my midwifery partner, and I had a home birth practice with a sliding scale fee. We were also open to barters, as we believed that our work had a value and enjoyed the benefits and talents of our patients who sometimes were unable to pay.

Jan was an artist, so we agreed that she would create paintings for us in lieu of payment. She seemed excited with the barter. She told us she would complete her art pieces before the birth of her child. She also stated she painted pieces spontaneously and that her best works came without a preconceived plan of action, but when she was open to inspiration. We trusted her process. She seemed to trust ours.

Once she decided to transfer her care to our practice, she seemed eager to learn everything about birth. She never missed an appointment. She found New Mother groups and plunged herself into birth books. She knew no one personally who had given birth at home, but seemed confidant in her ability to do so and, yet, was simultaneously vulnerable in her current living situation. Another contrast she seemed resigned to.

She gained adequate weight and had few discomforts except the occasional fatigue after working her shift as a waitress. Her belly grew, her face softened. Her short white hair began to grow dark roots, but she seemed content with the contrast.

Jan came to her appointment during her eighth month of pregnancy to present us with two black canvases; white outlines of figures depicting a woman in bondage.

She seemed pleased with her choice and desire to shock us and she did succeed indeed do so. We suspected she might have reasons for creating the pieces and explored further the possibilities of a history of rape or abuse, her current relationship… the usual suspects for disturbing behavior. She denied that she had any history of sexual abuse or physical abuse, but did believe her current relationship left her feeling isolated and alone. We agreed to discuss further her emotional state, but were also honest with her. We could not accept the paintings as barter.

Val and I, despite our openness to bartering, had to value the barter in order for there to be an exchange. The paintings would never be hung in our homes, they would never be cherished and therefore, we couldn't accept them. For a moment, she balked at the suggestions that we would not accept them as they were. Then she accused us of not accepting her for who she was. We explained that as we saw it, she was not accepting us for who we were and that we felt her paintings were not in the spirit of the barter. We agreed that we would give her additional time to execute additional paintings. We suggested that her next attempt could be birth-related as we both already had collections of birth-related art. Reluctantly, Jan agreed.

During her ninth month of pregnancy, she came for her usual appointment. She offered two wood cuts of women in labor; the woodcuts had a black background, with motifs of a sun and birthing women in each. Although, colorless, the details and craft were pleasant and would fit nicely my collection of birth art. She seemed bored by her effort. We accepted the wood cuts as barter.

Her contractions began at 2 a.m. We arrived at her apartment, nested in a narrow three-flat building. To get to her apartment, we had to go up a narrow stairway and then knocked on a door with peeling paint. Her boyfriend, half awake and half dressed, greeted us and led us through the apartment where we found Jan sitting in the bathroom. She looked around the room, taking in our arrival and nodding at us to acknowledge our presence. She closed her eyes. She continued her nocturnal labor, occasionally whimpering with the contractions, shut up in the bathroom while the faucet dripped in the background. It was summer, and the bathroom window allowed a cool breeze. People passed in the street below despite the late hour. She seemed in deep thought, unaware of these distractions and vaguely aware of our presence. We offered her sips of water and occasionally tea with honey. She drank in silence.

The room next to the bathroom was sweetly lit by two windows and the street light from outside. Clean, neat, and pleasant, but void of colors. There was a small cradle beside her futon bed on the floor. A pile of birth books were neatly piled up against the wall, and a crate was filled with infant clothes were neatly arranged.

Her labor soon fell into a routine. She seemed overcome by the drowsiness during transitional stage, when the endorphins lure women to sleep. It was as if she were somewhere else. She was sleeping without dreaming. A contraction would come and Jan would get up and pace around the apartment, returning to the bathroom, allowing us to sit only on the edge of its entrance.

She seemed to move through birth without fear. She continued her labor pacing, stopping with each contraction, grasping and holding out for a grip of a hand with each of us. We obliged and offered her our hands. She would squeeze them in silence, her eyes closed.

Finally, she realized she could no longer control the contractions and no longer held her hand out for a grasp. The contractions demanded that she make some adjustments, that she surrender, and trust birth, but she began to rebel.

Wildness took over. She began to howl. She felt split in two, her moans echoing in the room, partly ignited by fear and partly driven from wells deep inside that were also integral to who she was: the essence of birth, knowing you better by forgetting the face worn on a daily basis. She moved beyond an easy definition of herself to the place we go at our birth and our death. The rage, fear, and abuse that might have shaped the experience of her young life were finding a new meaning that called for an oasis from the former self.

Jan allowed us to nurture her during the contractions with warm packs and counter-pressures. She accepted a scented bath we drew for her. As she stepped into the bath and had her next contractions, her screams died down, and she sank into surrender, seeming to find her true self. Her moans were loud, but genuine.

She emerged from the bath a confident birthing woman. She seemed to know her strength while acknowledging her vulnerability. Within a couple more contractions, she felt an urge to push. Her efforts were steady, we coaxed her on, and she accepted our directions. As the baby emerged from the vaginal opening, Jan reached down to touch her daughter's head. She opened her eyes and her eyes met ours, and she smiled, delighted at herself and her progress. A couple more pushes. She seemed stronger and more empowered by each contraction. With each contraction, each push, she became more active, more present. Her often pale face was flushed with color, and Jan seemed to flourish in the moment, accepting labor as the ultimate contest. She seemed to make a choice to dwell within the moment, as if this birth was her most creative piece of work.

The bulge of her perineum burned, she howled, and the baby crowned. We lifted her daughter Lily up to her and she accepted the newborn as the conclusion of our barter. Jan smiled proudly at her infant and seemed no longer to struggle to move ahead toward a new expression of a maternal self. We could imagine her as a mother; she could fully take action and responsibility for her infant.

After the birth, we followed Jan for several months. She often stopped by my home-based office for breastfeeding support, and enjoyed breastfeeding. She nursed for over a year. Soon afterwards, she reconciled with her estranged mother and returned home for more support.

Two years after her departure, I received a postcard that she had delivered a second child and was married to a wonderful man. Jan had returned to school to continue to study art and found a supportive community of friends.

It was a spring day; I parked my car at the end of the block. As I approached my house, I saw a young mother sitting on my front porch swing. She had two small children with her and a brown bag with a large item inside. As I walked toward my front walk, I could see that the woman was Jan, her daughter Lily by her side, and an infant on her lap. I was surprised by her presence and stated as such, "What a surprise, what brings you back here?" She reached down in the brown bag and presented the most beautiful colorful birth painting. "I never paid you back" she replied.

The Woman who Consciously Abandoned Herself

Feighiannon came to us one autumn when she was three months pregnant with her second child. Feighiannon was not her birth name; her birth name was Laura, a name she claimed did not resonate with her. Feighiannon was not phonetically pronounced; the accent is supposedly on the first syllable. I often mispronounced it, as I am prone to do even with much easier names. She would accept no nicknames. So I stumbled often, she corrected me often, and so went the beginnings of our communication.

She and her husband had arrived from Idaho hoping to make the Midwest their new home. To me, they were a visually off-putting couple. Her husband wore a long overcoat despite the Indian summer, which he liked to flap almost like a vampire would. She was taller than he by about a foot, long and lean, but with a potbelly. She laughed easily, despite numerous stories of hardships. She had a brother who had died of cancer a decade before and a mother who refused to accept either her son's diagnosis or his death. Feighiannon's mother's grief led her to take her own life. Feighiannon had been fifteen at the time, and newly responsible for raising her three younger sisters. Her father was grief-stricken and emotionally crippled. One by one, each of the children matured and moved from Idaho. A few were in California, a few went north to Canada. The Midwest was an ideal new place to begin, she explained, a place clear of her history where she knew no one.

Mike, her husband, described his family as appearing normal, but the real truth was quite the opposite, he said. He held a somewhat paranoid belief that each secretly plotted to avoid any communication with each other, despite outward appearances of togetherness. They went together to church every Sunday. They spoke to each other at church gatherings and social functions, but rarely spoke to each other at home. He claimed as a child at Boy Scout camp he was lost in the woods for several hours and no thought to send a rescue team. His father was the Boy Scout leader. He eventually found his way back to base camp. This was the only story Mike told us about his past, about his life.

But they appeared to be good parents and to enjoy parenting. Feighiannon and Mike brought their four-year-old son to every visit. While Mike doted on their son, Feighiannon shared more agonizing tales. She feared her own pain would lead to depression; she always passed the Edinburgh screening for depression and seemed pleased that we often followed up with concerns if she had moments of insomnia. She always stayed within the parameters of "normal" and while she didn't feel normal, she had little interest in medication or therapy. She had tried both in the past. "I've moved beyond the darkest points in my life," she said.

Mike took care of their son during these conversations. He occasionally tried his hand at humor, but it was often flat and without a coherent punch line. He seemed comfortable with awkward pauses. They had a sweet family dynamic despite their alienation.

Feighiannon said her last birth felt disconnected. She had a chosen a hospital midwife birth, and, having wanted a natural childbirth, endured most of her labor without medication. Towards the end of labor, she had accepted Stadol, a painkiller. The effects of the drug made her drowsy, and she could remember little of her labor, a fact she found unsettling. She also felt that although she had chosen a midwife for her birth, she ended up with a midwife whom she did not know and one who could not pronounce her name. The midwife was disinterested in mastering the first syllable. It was evident to both of them that they would never meet again following the birth.

Feighiannon and Mike very clearly told me their intentions. They both hoped the midwifery service would increase their chances of a natural birth and the ability to know their providers. They found both the midwives and Midwest welcoming and were excited for a new start on life.

As Feighiannon's pregnancy progressed, she had occasional intense visits with me. She struggled with the notion of a family and maintaining close relationships. She felt Mike was indeed her best friend, and intellectually felt satisfied by their relationship, yet she had so many moments that she felt physically low, dull, and blocked from fully accepting his support. She recited again her story of a sickly brother who prematurely died, a mother who had killed herself, a depressed father, how often she wanted to run away, but she always stayed to care for her father and siblings. She could remember sitting up at night, wanting to cry, but no one would be there to console her, so she would just sit up quietly, alone in her grief, and would promise herself to make it another day and another night and eventually she no longer felt the pain. We revisited these memories over and over, and she eventually agreed to accept counseling. We continued to support her, but encouraged her to find emotional health as our skills were limited for her needs.

Other mothers I had met with incredibly painful pasts had one thing in common: they struggled to make even the smallest strides toward healing. Feighiannon, however, seemed to neither transcend all that happened nor to embrace crisis. She seemed neither to try to control events nor was she passive. She was neither needy nor abstruse. She was easy to be with, yet her outer self seemed indifferent to her internal self. She was alienated from her own sense of being.

Feighiannon lived somewhere between hurt and anger, despair and hope. She stood in a nowhere zone, an island unto herself and within herself.

The only times she seemed to be present was in her parenting. She seemed to truly enjoy her son, especially when he made her laugh, and her laughs from his antics were belly laughs. She would glance over at him during a visit, he'd catch her eye and perform an impish routine that would delight her. She named him after her brother.

Feighiannon and Mike started labor on a dark spring dawn, ready to have a baby. We darkened the room and lit a few candles. She seemed alone despite the presence of her husband and the midwives. As the contractions grew in intensity, they seemed to weigh her down, not so much from the pain, but that which was left unsaid. The room was heavy with things unexpressed. She paced the room, walking both simultaneously somewhere and nowhere. Not certain where she was going, she requested to be checked. It was now 7 a.m., she was 7cm dilated, 100-percent effaced, and at 0 station. Feighiannon requested to go into the birthing tub. The heat of the water made the pain tolerable, she said. As she sank further into the tub, her arms draped over the sides, she accepted cool cloths to her forehead and requested that the window be propped open so that a light touch of the morning breeze could slip through the window. The chirps of morning birds soothed her. She seemed thankful for the coolness as it relieved the waves of heat produced by the heavy labor. She said she felt slightly nauseous, and then suddenly she began to heave.

She reached out and clung to her husband, who was seated on a chair beside the birth tub. She trembled with contractions. She lowered her head, her eyes downcast, and curled up in the tub like a child herself. I let her go into that personal place all mothers must enter before birth. She began to weep—tears of weariness, tears of relief, tears of sadness and regret. She wept with all her strength, as if exhausted from years of not weeping.

I applauded her courage and remarked, "Feighiannon, you are so strong."

She corrected me, and this time not for my pronunciation of her name. "Mary," she replied, "I am not strong; I survive. I know the difference."

Her words caused me to pause and reflect. She stated a truth and yet, she was underestimating herself because something kept her moving on from day to day. "To continue is your path. Take courage; it is your strength."

At that moment, her face relaxed, and she looked both vulnerable and strong. She held out her hand and gripped both me and her husband. She climbed out of the tub, she shook, she cried. It was obvious the contractions brought on both terror and progress. Her heart beat faster, her breath became a steady pant, and some new essence—perhaps courage—lit her from the inside. She dropped to her knees. As the baby exited her body, she rejoiced in a jubilant cry, "It's coming…the baby is coming."

She delivered in the hands and knees position. Mike joined the midwives in delivering the child and placing the baby between Feighiannon's legs so that she could discover the sex. She laughed.

"It's a boy" she announced, radiant and proud.

She brought her son to her arms and he began to smack his lips and root toward her breasts. She began to breastfeed him. We propped a few pillows behind her and she smiled at us. She had a sense of peace about herself that had not been there before. She had moved through her disconnect from sense of self, apathy and alienation.

Natural childbirth forces us to move inward and greet the nooks and crannies of our interior being, where the self merges with the many. "I" becomes "us" as we sense that this solo act is part of a larger cosmic dance. Hence, we become one with infinity and therefore, can no longer feel alone, for we have the felt experience of being part of the whole. Feighiannon had become part of the larger global tribe and was beginning to embrace her membership.

When Angels Sing

Singing is a natural way for anyone to bring the power and energy of sound into her life. All living things have a natural urge to sing. Humans and other mammals, birds, insects and even the great, extinct wooly mammoth sing special songs to call their children home. Though singing is universal, many people feel uncomfortable singing, as if we'll be judged the moment we expose our voices.

I know this feeling quite well. When I was a child, I was told by a music teacher not to sing at an Easter celebration, but rather to lip sync as my classmates sang. He announced to the class that my voice was not suitable for Sunday choir. Apparently, I was tone deaf and my voice was flat and off key. That is not my only experience of a teacher asking me not sing. I was told at a few grade school Christmas concerts to mouth the words instead of sing, as well. These childhood memories were responsible for my perception that singing was only for those with "good" voices, and my limited enjoyment of song as a way to celebrate life.

In general, I have always found my voice disagreeable to hear on voice-mails or tape recordings. That said, I once was pleasantly complimented when a former client and her daughter heard my voice in a parking lot. She told her daughter "Let's follow that voice. That woman was at your birth." When she told me that, it gave me a sense that our voices are more than nasal, flat or low. They can convey so much more when feelings are held within their tone, for better or worse.

Despite experiencing a few instances of negative feedback over the years about my singing ability, I believe strongly that song is a way of lifting the spirit, that singing is the best exercise for a healthy soul. And it is particularly crucial for women in labor.

A woman in labor can find so much strength when she finds her voice. I have heard women scream, moan, howl, and shout as they pushed their babies into the world. But the most extraordinary example of a woman finding her voice in labor was when Ki brought her whole church choir to her labor to sing her baby into the world.

Ki chose us for both her first and second births. At the time of her second birth, she already had a tight community of other mothers she called her "sister friends." They often got together to share stories, care for each other's children and sing. She lived on the far south side of Chicago, and by the time my associate Trish and myself arrived, Ki's "sisters" had already assumed many of the duties of labor support and midwifery.

Most impressively, they were singing—all at once and differently—polyrhythms, bird-like sounds, and sweet melodies. The sisters wore long dresses and headscarves in multiple colors. They raised their arms as they swayed in song, like one unified wave. Every voice was both distinct and part of the whole. Ki moaned. They sang harmony and carried her beyond her discomfort. She even sang with them, sometimes setting the tone herself and they would follow; other times they would lead and she follow. She seemed to understand that the act of singing, of living in song, would both soothe and energize the deepest, most capable part of herself.

At times, her song sounded agonizing. The sisters rocked her in their arms. As Ki's contractions increased in intensity, the sisters moved toward her and created a circle, their foreheads nearly touched each other's. They all fit together.

Ki faced her final contractions by belting out a sound that went higher and higher, *AH, AH, AH*. The sisters followed with complex and intertwining melodies. The whole room sounded like a tropical forest with multitudes of birds chirping, singing and crowing. They were a most magnificent choir of women, mothers, friends, daughters, and wives.

The sound vibrations created ten times more support than what anyone could create alone. The whole community cooed the baby down. Ki stretched her arms out and swayed, and they swayed with her. Both Trish and I stood speechless. I was a tad giddy inside, feeling the groove, the melody of the women. It made me realize just how much we repress within ourselves, the gifts of letting our spirits out through song. I once read of a granny midwife who hummed the babies out and rocked herself as she prepared for their deliveries. What would delivery rooms be like if the chorus of women were allowed and encouraged to sing? What would staff members' morale be if they could sing while they worked?

Ki's husband sat behind her. He did not sing, instead moving his head with the rhythm of the song. As the baby descended, her sisters reached in to catch the infant. Trish and I handed them warm blankets and Ki and her sisters caught her second daughter Mia. Mia looked up at the community of women and let out her own first song.

Clearing the Way

While working in Chicago, I was approached by the director of a midwifery training program and maternity hospital in Mexico. The program was designed to provide training to midwives on providing culturally appropriate care to Mexico's indigenous people.

They felt that cooperation between midwives and doctors was essential for reducing maternal mortality. The hospital employed traditional midwives who worked side by side with physicians. The students would learn from both providers. The midwifery program was a three-year education program, similar to many European models of midwifery education. The hospital employed traditional midwives, as well. In addition to working in the hospital, students would be sent to work in rural areas to assist traditional midwives. The students would learn to give massages during labor and allow a woman to give birth in a squatting position, if she so desired, which was uncommon in most Mexican hospitals. The program also recruited daughters of traditional midwives, so that the future of rural midwifery would become more professional and evidence based. It would also be more culturally appropriate and reduce the unnecessary medical interventions often found in medical models of obstetrics.

Prior to the program graduating its own students, it was discovered that there was a gap in the practice and understanding of the two models of maternity care. Therefore, the director looked for a compatible partner to begin an exchange program that would strengthen their model of training, and also strengthen perspectives of traditional midwifery held by other birth providers in the United States who were serving Mexican communities.

At the time, I was a co-director of a nurse-midwifery service at a community health center that served a large Mexican immigrant population in Chicago. Our practice had a multidisciplinary approach, working with community women as doulas and breastfeeding peer counselors, nurse-midwives and certified professional midwives and physicians.

In addition, we were one of the few institutions serving the Mexican population to provide both home and hospital deliveries. The practice used the community approach of the home visit to provide postpartum care. The midwives were bi-lingual in Spanish and English. We had several Mexican-born community women participating in our birth assistant training program, and we seemed like a good fit for a partnership with the midwifery training program in Mexico.

The director of the practice was invited to visit Mexico and discuss the possibility of coordinating an exchange program between the two organizations. I would coordinate with the director, staff, and students from Mexico the arrangements for the visit and for the work they would perform with the Chicago midwives and physicians, as well as our staff and birth assistant students, many of whom were from Mexico, who would work and train in Mexico. It sounded like a good plan.

When I arrived in Mexico, I was greeted by a petite American midwife, who happened to be a nun and home birth midwife. She was a certified professional midwife, had learned most of her trade as an apprentice midwife . She identified herself as a traditional midwife. She is also Native American and has a deep respect for ancestral wisdom. She had moved to Mexico on a temporary basis and volunteered her time at the maternity hospital as a midwife. She had a kind, gentle approach and had already formed a kinship with the traditional midwives on staff at the hospital. She was also familiar with the midwives working in the local rural communities, and was to be my guide during my visit. She spent several days familiarizing me with local customs and hospital policies.

The head midwife at the time was a traditional midwife, with many years of experience and a commanding presence. She looked me over, and asked me a few questions in Spanish. My Spanish is basic, although I can hold a conversation and have a good comprehension of the language. I am not a native speaker and my accent is strongly American despite years of practice. I am sure my grammar choices would annoy a native speaker. Unlike my Mexican midwife guide, I am not petite. I stand 5 feet 8 inches tall and was a head taller than most of the patients and the traditional midwives.

The head midwife was not petite either. She looked strong, her arms and shoulders ready to deliver any infant stuck in the vaginal canal. She was compact and grounded in her stance. She seemed older than me, with a slight graying of the hair at her temples. At first, she seemed defensive, explaining to me that she had little formal education. I asked a few questions for honest inquiry, although I have been told in my own cultural context I can be in "interview mode" when meeting someone for the first time. I try not to overwhelm, but this can be a challenge.

I liked her despite her not seeming especially warm to me. She had a presence that demanded respect. She seemed confident in herself and in her skills. Observing her a few days at the hospital and clinic, it was clear she was the "go to" person for staff and beloved by the patients. She momentarily took pity on me when she realized my knowledge of herbs was bleak; she observed first-hand in the hospital garden that I couldn't identify an orange tree from a lemon tree.

One day, the American midwife invited me, my two young daughters, and a visiting student from Europe on a day trip. We were to accompany the head midwife to a local village, with several of us riding in the company's van, driven by her husband. Other passengers included the American midwife guide, the European student, my two daughters, and me. I believe the young European student (I can't remember what country she was from) was studying anthropology, and so was invited along to observe in that context.

Once we arrived, the village midwife showed us around her home clinic and village, which consisted of a few homes, chicken coops, and dirt roads. We returned to her home, where she and our lead midwife announced that we would be experiencing a *limpia* performed by the local healer. A *limpia* is an ancient spiritual healing practice.

I sensed that I would be a bit out of my comfort zone. Despite some customs of the "evil eye" lingering within the Mexican communities of Chicago, most immigrants acclimate to the customs of previous generations of Mexican Americans living in Chicago rather quickly. The more urban the immigrant and the more years spent in United States, the less these traditions are evident when interacting with Midwestern American midwives. For instance, later, when our Mexican-born students arrived for the exchange program, they would be referred by our Mexican guest as "American." The nuances of these distinctions can be lost on me and yet, I am constantly intrigued to discover them. I happen to love being placed in new cultural settings, but the process of getting out of one's own element can be challenging. I had a sinking feeling that the *limpia* was intended to put me out of my comfort zone.

They began with gathering the needed herbs and eggs; I was not able to identify any of the plants. My midwife-home birth nun guide was invited by the head midwife to assist in preparation of the ritual. So one by one, they had the student, then the nun, and then my eldest daughter close their eyes. The midwife brushed their bodies with the tree branches and spoke softly. I am unsure of the steps in the ritual, but it lasted about twenty minutes. It ended with rubbing a whole egg around each person's auric field, while the person receiving the *limpia* sat still, eyes closed. The midwife blew energy into her cupped hands intermittently. A glass of water was placed in the center and the egg was cracked into the water glass. If the egg sank to the bottom and the water was clear, then this was translated into verification that no evil spirits surrounded the person. Each of the other guests passed the egg test.

The lead midwife was suspicious about my presence. There had been several other midwives from the United States who had visited for short-term assistance. They often had quick answers and seemed rushed, or so I was told by my guide. Moreover, there exists everywhere a schism between those who are traditionally trained, skilled birth attendants, certified professional midwives, and certified nurse-midwives. Each believes her own orientation to midwifery is more authentic or better qualified than the other's. The lead midwife, whom I would later come to know well, is one of the finest midwives I've seen despite her dearth of formal education.

I felt my stomach sink as she choose me to rub the egg around my aura. Unlike the other "egg rolls," which had been handled with care, she shook my egg vigorously and then opened it into the water. She seemed pleased with the resulting murky yellow glass. The other midwife responded on cue, claiming that I had evil spirits and that she was to seek a young maiden who was pure and could receive the spirits from me. Promptly, a woman, not so young and of questionable purity, appeared. I had been had and there was nothing I could do about it.

The lead midwife smirked, pleased with herself.

I responded with my own smirk, "I know I am a good person, I am just a midwife doing the best I can."

She seemed a bit softer in her reply, "I know, we take in a lot as midwives." She assured me that they could help me—for a price of $30 extra dollars. (I had already paid $40 for the *limpia*).

I may not always understand the nuances, but I do get the obvious. I was both fascinated and hurt by the many levels of reality that coexisted within the unfriendly welcome I was receiving and yet, I knew on a strange level that this was also a welcoming or a hazing similar to a joining a sorority.

I did not dismiss the fact that on one level, the village midwife didn't trust me. She believed my methods were modern and therefore wrong, and that I lacked the actual education needed to be a real midwife. Her way of proclaiming me different was to claim I carried psychic impurity on my person.

On the other hand, I understood a few nuances from my work in Chicago working in a Mexican community. There is an idea of the patron. The director at our agency, who enjoyed the role of the patron, often used the Mexican saying "There can only be one boyfriend," to place an emphasis on loyalty and honor to her, the patron. The rules were clear; if I was to proceed, I should put aside my hurt from the symbolic exclusion. She had set the stage to use her tools to proclaim a cultural distinction, to reject me while simultaneously accepting me, but nevertheless reinforce symbolic boundaries between the two of us. In short, she had pulled rank—no differently than an obstetrician telling a woman that she is unfit to deliver normally, performing an unnecessary procedure, and then charging her extra for it.

Each paradigm—Certified Professional Midwives (CPM) and Certified Nurse Midwives (CNM)—can work in isolation, thus becoming even further alienated from the other. I had often lived between these two paradigms in my work in the United States as a CPM working among CNMs. I found that more boundaries seemed to have been set by other CPMs than by other midwives. Though we are both in the same marginal profession, the habit of recreating a boundary between one type of midwife and another is a way to exercise occupational prestige. I had grown weary of the polarization in the States and perhaps romanticized that Mexican midwifery would be more pure. I walked right into the trap in that rural village.

What is "reality," except for the rules and customs of understanding and behaving that makes a person or culture believe it to be real? In truth, I am not perfect, and a curse had been cast upon me by an unstable woman at work a few weeks prior to my trip. I had a staff member from Central America who was caught stealing and falsifying her time sheet. As mentioned before, I had few interactions with the "evil eye" working in Chicago, but each event was memorable. The staff member was terminated. As she parted, she cursed me with the "evil eye." This curse was apparently still with me on my visit to Mexico.

If I decided not to be offended by the village midwife's proclamation—and instead adopt her world view—something good could come from it. There seemed no point in taking this incident more personally, even though they viewed me as the problem; doing so might only lead to further mistruths. Instead, I could decide to do my best. I could believe there must be some purpose behind my landing in a small mountain village, far from my home town, where I had recently received a curse and was recovering from a hard year at work. Instead, I could receive the gift of being cleansed.

I patiently sat and allowed them to send my bad spirits off. I paid the money to the local midwife. Certainly, she appreciated the lead midwife's ability to increase her weekly earnings. They proceeded with their ceremony and proclaimed me clean.

I returned to the United States shortly after, and began to organize an exchange program, as I had promised. In the next few months, ten Mexican staff members and midwifery students came to Chicago for several weeks. This was no small task on either end—finding housing, coordinating lectures, exploring clinical opportunities and, for some of our guests, getting visas for the first time. Nevertheless, we successfully put a system in place.

A few months later, I returned to Mexico to assist at the hospital clinic. During that time, several of the traditional midwives had left the hospital because heir families had not adjusted to their doing shift work. Therefore, the hospital was short staffed and anxious for some relief.

I rang the hospital bell, and the same lead midwife greeted me warmly. As she was leaving on vacation the next day, she gave me a quick orientation, and then informed me that I would be the only midwife on that night.

I protested, "Shouldn't someone work with me the first night?"

"You have experience with home births. You'll be fine," she assured me.

And off she went.

There were a few nurses on duty with me. It was a cold, quiet night and when I heard the door bell ring to the tiny hospital, I hopped out of bed and with the night nurse, opened the huge wooden door.

Yesenia came in, wearing flip flops with feet covered in mud from what was obviously a long walk to the hospital. She was definitely in heavy labor. The nurse handed me her chart. The chart noted that in her pregnancy she had a hemoglobin level of six, half her blood supply. She had lapsed while in care. She had several children in a succession that never allowed her body to fully recover. She was at risk for hemorrhage, a complication I would rather avoid. Her tired uterus was at risk for not being able to effectively contract after delivery. If she had come to her visits more regularly, there might have been opportunity to treat her in advance with iron, but now it was too late. She was about to deliver.

The nurse led her to the delivery room. I braced myself and prepared Pitocin to be given by IM injection in hope that this measure would help the uterus contract following delivery. I could hear my dear midwife friend, Anne Gallagher, saying "Give Pitocin with the delivery of the posterior shoulder if you suspect hemorrhage," something unfamiliar to home-birth midwives in the States, who screen out women with low hemoglobin levels for home births. The nurse rolled her eyes as I explained my plan of action.

The delivery was fast and uncomplicated. I cleansed the injection site of her left thigh with alcohol and plunged the needle in with one quick movement. I drew back on the plunger to see if a vein had been entered. No blood came up, so I injected slowly, pushing the plunger all the way down. I withdrew the needle and applied pressure to the site with a cotton ball, then waited for the placenta. I asked the nurse to set up an IV.

The afterbirth followed. Yesina began to feel severe cramps, the placenta delivered, and I had just begun to massage the uterus when there was a suddenly gush of blood. I immediately compressed the womb, inserting the edge of one of my hands beneath the womb on the abdominal wall, just above the bone that marked the lower limit of the abdominal wall. My other hand was firmly placed above the womb. There I was, somewhere in the foothills of the Sierra Madre, holding a womb between my two hands, the mother's fate lying in my ability to induce the uterus to contract.

The nurse was busy gathering clothes in which to dress the baby. I encouraged her to assist me with giving an injection of Methagine, as my hands were occupied. I also asked the nurse to assist the baby with nursing at the breast, which would also encourage the uterus to contract. The uterus began to bleed each time I attempted to release my hold. Reluctantly, she obliged. I told her that she would also need to call for the back-up physician, who was asleep at home, but who might need to come in for an operative procedure if the bleeding could not be controlled.

Oddly, Yesina never looked neither faint nor loss any consciousness, nor looked chilly, sweaty, pale, or weak, as other woman who had loss blood can look. She remained focused, and even smiled through much of the ordeal. Fortunately, the bleeding subsided and the uterus remained hardened. The nurse condescendingly asked if I still wanted the doctor called in. Her tone suggested that she could see that I was unused to the trials and tribulations that the courageous Mexican midwives faced on a daily basis. She was right, and I felt humbled by the experience and thankful I had received the *limpia*.

Over a decade has passed since my first trip. The exchange program went on for a few summers. Eventually, the exchange program was no longer needed. The Midwifery School successfully graduated professional midwives, who now work throughout Mexico, providing evidence-based, quality care. I continue to serve proudly as an advisory board member to this outstanding organization.

Miracle On Kedvale

We met Elizabeth as a pregnant, young immigrant who had been sent from Mexico to live with her relatives in Chicago, a foreign land. She had enraged her family by falling in love—the wrong thing to do, as far as they were concerned, for a poor girl from a broken home. Her mother had died in an auto accident when she was four. Her father, not recovered from his wife's death, drank often and eventually left the family for another woman.

Elizabeth's three elder brothers had left home a long time ago to seek better fortunes up north. So Elizabeth lived with her aunt and uncle in Mexico just above the poverty line. She fell in love with a young man in her town, they secretly courted each other, and she became pregnant (sort of Romeo and Juliet) and he joined her brothers north. Elizabeth's pregnancy added another burden to her relatives and they sent her north to stay with another set of relatives.

She had never met these Chicago relatives. She knew no English, had never lived in an urban setting, and had no means of caring for herself. She was seven months pregnant when she began care at the clinic where our team of midwives worked. I first met Elizabeth on a home visit after she had given birth with the help our hospital practice. She and her elderly relatives seemed trapped by their desperate circumstances—they lived in an old house with uneven steps, few pieces of furniture, broken windows, and no money for repairs. She was housed in a room slightly larger than a closet in their basement. The basement was dark and damp, and only a small window let in any light from the outside.

Basia, another midwife, and I worked with the family over time to cultivate tolerance and compassion. I'm not sure of all Basia's tricks, but she has a special gift for working with people on a daily basis with the kind of humor, love, and compassion that becomes contagious. Eventually, the family understood that it was necessary that Elizabeth be accepted and that she and the baby needed to be brought upstairs.

Shortly after the first baby was born, Elizabeth became pregnant again. No one seemed to know who the father was, but the family, while frustrated, had grown compassionate. They had moved to a larger 3-bedroom apartment, which they shared with Elizabeth.

However, Elizabeth seemed to have regressed in her mothering skills and still appeared clueless about mothering. She gave her new baby solid foods at one week of age. She forgot how often babies had to be fed, giggled when asked questions about cord care, and didn't know any bathing basics.

Basia, determined to stay with Elizabeth regardless of how much patience it took, set the young woman up with a teen program. She saw in Elizabeth a young, but capable, woman. She encouraged Elizabeth to strive to improve her mothering, supported her in breastfeeding and instructed her in child development. I personally wondered how Elizabeth would fare as a mother. Fortunately for her, the teen program would follow her for three years and her family seemed more willing and capable then the first time around.

Elizabeth felt uncomfortable with too much attention from others. She giggled nervously, and often bowed her head to the side before covering her mouth with her hand when she spoke. But despite all of her hard life circumstances, Elizabeth was not a bitter person. She never complained. She acknowledged that her life was hard, and she understood that her relatives were also stressed by life's circumstances. She knew that they were not obliged to take care of her or her children. In short, she had respect for and perspective on the difficulty of the situation.

She also remained steadfast in her loyalty to the mysterious young man who was the father or her children. He had left money for her and the baby, which helped Elizabeth's relatives better accept him. But neither he nor Elizabeth had the finances for a wedding, so the family forbade him to live with them.

He apparently shared an apartment with some other young, undocumented immigrant men. Since he was rarely visible, he remained an enigma to me.

* * *

Several years later, I was called to a home birth of a mother having her third child. The home was a four-bedroom Georgian in a well-established South Side neighborhood. When I entered the home and was greeted by a nanny, I was surprised; few community midwife patients could afford a nanny and such a prosperous home. I was the back-up midwife. I greeted the primary midwife, Abbey, who told me that the woman would soon be delivering.

The labor progressed rapidly, and soon after I arrived, the woman delivered a healthy 7-pound baby girl, with her husband and two children in attendance. Her husband broke out a bottle of champagne, and the birth team and family toasted the new mother. As I began to fill out the birth certificate and ask the mother questions to complete the form, she initially seemed uncomfortable with answering. When I asked her maiden name, she hesitated and bowed her head to the side, then covered her mouth with her hand. I couldn't believe it.

"Elizabeth, did you used to live on South Kedvale?"

She shyly nodded her head. "Yes, you visited me when I had my other children. With this pregnancy, my friends encouraged me to go to a private physician, but I knew I had to return to the clinic and the midwives. The midwives believed in me when no one else did."

I was overwhelmed and overjoyed. This unexpected blessing of becoming reacquainted with Elizabeth after she had struggled with years of hardship, was one of the gifts of my profession. Elizabeth and her family had come into an abundant harvest. Her boyfriend had worked as a busboy, then apprenticed as a chef, and refined his skills to become a top chef at a prestigious restaurant. When his income increased, he married Elizabeth.

I cherish this story, and her story does not stand alone. So much of the time, as birth providers, we only see a glimpse of anyone's life. Had we only known Elizabeth through her first birth or last birth, we would not have understood her triumphs. Hope is contagious; it changes the status quo and creates new realities.

Life Blood

had the opportunity to visit my sister, a physician in Malawi, Africa, and work with some of the finest midwives I have ever known. To be a midwife in Malawi is quite daunting. A midwife not only has to attend to women at risk of dying and who have few resources and are often malnourished, but she also at times must work with a shortage of medication, sterile equipment, and clean water. For mothers with high-risk pregnancies, the midwife needs to plan for their transportation from the villages with poor roads. In the rainy season, they need back-up plans for power outages. To my amazement, the staff was quite skilled at handling all sorts of emergencies. These midwives were extremely organized. There wasn't a single mother during my stay who didn't have a prenatal chart or have her blood type or HIV status noted. There wasn't a single midwife who wasn't ready to deliver optimal care.

It can still be a struggle to succeed. The hospital continues to be able to buy essential medicines, despite the government occasionally being late in paying the baseline salaries of most of the employees. Nevertheless, the staff perseveres. The number of physicians in the area is close to rock bottom. My sister is the only doctor working full time at the hospital for a catchment area of more than 200,000 people.

There is a shortage of other formally trained health personnel, as well. This widens the boundaries of who performs what procedures. Staff have to be able to perform C-sections to save the lives of mothers and babies at every hospital, at any time. At Embangweni Hospital, where my sister worked, C-sections are mainly done by clinical officers with four years of training. They are assisted by patient attendants who have 12 weeks of schooling, plus continual on-the-job training. Sometimes they have to work with women with late-stage AIDS or malaria who need C-sections. Despite these challenges, the hospital does better in outcomes for mothers than the national average, where one in fifty women in Malawi who have C-sections dies.

During my visit, a mother delivered twins. The risk of fetal mortality increases with twins. These twins were born after 36 weeks, which improved their survival rate, but the first twin was much larger than the second, a worrisome situation. The second twin began to suffer from the reduction of the uterine capacity after the birth of the first baby, and then from lack of oxygen. The second twin also assumed a transverse lie and had to be delivered by C-section. This mother was already anemic and had lost considerable blood during the surgery.

By definition, loss of over 500 ml of blood during the first 24 hours constitutes postpartum hemorrhage. Grace, the Malawian mother, was still unstable. She was alert, but had a rapid and weak pulse. A key to her treatment was transfusion of blood. The amount had to be adequate to replace at least the amount lost, and she needed the transfusion quickly.

If she were to die, her children would be left vulnerable; there would be no one to breastfeed these newborns, and it would mean an additional burden on her family to provide basic care to her other surviving children .

When we were in Lilongwe, the capital city of Malawi, we stayed briefly with a friend of my sister's who ran an orphanage for children whose mothers have died in childbirth, a sobering thought for those of us living in resource-rich countries. One of the children there, a 3-year-old boy, has an uncertain future. He has returned to his village three times, but he eventually has come back to the orphanage because he has been neglected and suffered from severe malnutrition. The clothes given to him beyond a tee shirt were stripped from him. In his particular village, there is no one to care for him. Sometimes orphaned children are stigmatized. The best long-term plan for orphans is to care for mothers, especially in childbirth, to reduce the likelihood of orphaning more children.

I didn't expect my sister to approach me about donating blood. Of course, it was a no brainer; I would donate. I confessed to my sister that I had never given blood before and explained that I was either breastfeeding or pregnant. My sister corrected my false sense of reasoning. "Natalia [my youngest] is 14."

Despite being in the medical profession, needles going into me make me a little queasy. I do not seem to react to seeing blood in childbirth, but the sight of blood leaving my body makes me a tad light-headed. I took a deep breath and with that, proceeded to the hospital lab to have my blood typed, cleared for HIV and hepatitis, and then matched for the transfusion.

As the lab technician placed the needle in the vein and adjusted it, I could feel myself get light-headed and told myself to look away. I could feel my blood pressure wanting to drop, and thought it wise to continue to lie still. I stared up at the ceiling, trying to keep my mind off the procedure. To my surprise, the procedure was quick. I lay there another few moments, gathering myself together, convincing myself not to be a hypochondriac, and not to have a vaso-vagal response. I intellectually knew everything was fine and kept saying to myself, "You're okay, you're okay". . I sat slowly up, sipped some water, and within a few minutes, was ready to leave.

As it turned out, my hemoglobin was 13, twice the level of the poor woman who had had a hemorrhage. I had more than enough blood to donate and yet, I had felt possessive for so many years of my blood. Blood is the staple of life; it is our internal life force. My blood had nourished my five children while they were fetuses; my blood had supplied my milk source while breastfeeding. Blood is probably the best gift we can give. I had extremely strong, healthy, and plentiful blood. And yet, it had taken me long to give this gift outside of my nuclear family.

An hour after my blood was removed, I went to visit the woman. We had met previously during her postpartum recovery. She was nursing her twins, a task difficult to do without adequate blood supply. My blood was still warm to the touch. A nurse reintroduced me to her and told her in her native language that it was my blood she was receiving. The woman reached out her hand and grasped mine tight. She spoke a few words in Tambuka, and the nurse translated back to me, She says, "Thank you, thank you very much!" The translations told me what her grasp had already conveyed.

There is a saying by expatriates that states, "Africa is like malaria; it gets into your blood." There is now a little of my blood in Africa. We are all blood sisters and brothers and can truly be one another's life force.

A Christmas Story

I have never understood why Christian birth providers often request the holidays off, assuming their more secular-leaning colleagues or non-Christian providers should deliver the Christmas babies. Isn't the point to make sure we are available to serve? To make room at the inn? If there is any holiday we should work, Christmas should be it. And so, I have often volunteered to work on this holiday. Needless to say, there are those moments during a long Christmas birth, when my eye glimpses the clock, and the image appears of my family sitting down to a delicious Christmas dinner without me, and I feel the distance between wanting to be with them and waiting to catch this Christmas baby.

That said, I have many of my fond memories of births around Christmas. Births next to Christmas trees with Christmas lights twinkling, snowflakes whispering against the window as a woman labors next to a warm fireplace, hazelnut candles burning on the mantel, the mother curled on the sofa with her husband, and me cradling a steaming mug of coffee as we wait. I picture children's amazed eyes at they greet a newborn sibling. Christmas births bring such extra joy; this is a wonderful life as a midwife.

Of course, I do my own special preparations for Christmas births. I keep a selection of Christmas CDs in the car. Christmas is the time of year I display my schmaltzy side. I particularly enjoy hokey renditions of Christmas songs. My particular favorite is Johnny Mathis singing *O Holy Night*. In my opinion, he has the best rendition of that song. My brother Ed, in true Sommers' spirit, once did eight recordings of *O Holy Night* as a gift to his siblings and ranked them in order of his favorites. He did not place Johnny first, and of course, I begged to disagree. I play Johnny's rendition repeatedly on my way to a birth, and it triggers so many warm memories of Christmas from my own past.

My dad was "Mr. Christmas," and responsible for so many of my fond holiday memories. He had grown up poor. His parents died when he was relatively young, but to hear my father tell stories of his childhood, you'd think he grew up with the Cleavers of *Leave It To Beaver* fame. His Christmas stories were always full of joy and hope, even though his brothers quit school to support the family. His family had a deep Christian faith, and he felt, even from a young age, that God had not forsaken them. This faith kept him going throughout his life and gave him hope, leaving a profound impression on us as children.

My dad loved Christmas as an opportunity to celebrate with his family; loved buying gifts for all the children; loved decorating. Putting up the family Christmas tree with Christmas songs in the background, decorating and baking Christmas cookies with my family was just the start. We also had an annual Christmas party; all the relatives would come over on December 23rd, when Santa would pay us a surprise visit during the festivities. On Christmas Eve, we would have a family day, go to midnight mass, and then on Christmas morning, Santa would return with more gifts. Later we would have Christmas dinner. There might have been other struggles and challenges throughout the year, but Christmas was a sacred time in our household.

I keep my Dad's sense of tradition (he has since passed away) as I prepare for my Christmas births. Modern birth often places so much emphasis on the routine without any spiritual development, so that as providers, we often forget to fall on our knees and hear the angel sing.

Christmas is an opportunity for us to remember that as midwives, we have witnessed God's grace in birth and to reaffirm our strong belief that women have the courage it takes to receive the grace of God and handle any situation that might arise. If we truly believe in the Christmas message, we have an obligation as birth attendants to guide women to accept that the divine dwells within them so that they can realize their ability, at the moment of their child's passage, to connect to a higher power. Christmas is a Christian's midwife most sacred holiday.

One Christmas night, I noticed the snow-laden trees leaning heavily onto my street as I started my car, scraped the windshield, and began my journey down to the Little Village neighborhood on the south side of Chicago. I put Johnny on to keep me company, and sipped some coffee mixed with eggnog from my mug.

I arrived in time to meet my fellow midwife, Anne. I have plenty of fond memories encountering my sister midwives in a parking lot at 2 a.m. to give them a break between consecutive births. One time, we gathered in the middle of the night, Carrie and Basia with their mug of coffees, and yes, their hand-rolled cigarettes, leaning against Carrie's pick-up truck. Oh yes, midwives are a hearty bunch. That memory always makes me laugh, perhaps because I love my sister midwives and all their idiosyncrasies.

This particular Christmas night was no exception. The drive across town wasn't without a few slides on the street. The snow was fresh and coming down steadily.

The apartment was on the third floor of a three-flat, and from the outside, looked uninhabited. The door bell was dead. We saw a light on the top floor, tossed a penny up on the window, and the husband, a wiry fellow, motioned that he would come down. When he opened the door to a pitch-black stairwell, we knew this wasn't a fluke, but the way they lived—in a poor neighborhood with faulty, old electrical wiring. He helped schlep our big bags full of equipment up the dark stairs. The door at the top of the stairs was opened a crack, revealing a sliver of brightness. Inside, a little Christmas tree sat on a table with a star on top, the source of light. Four presents for each of the couples' other children were tucked beneath.

Maria dozed but lifted her head to reveal a loving smile. As she sat up, a contraction began. She went on hands and knees on the bed, a simple mattress on a metal frame. The room was cool; only thinly glazed windows separated us from the cold, bitter winds outside. A few blankets served as curtains. She looked tired and yet, her smile after each contraction revealed a sense of peace and acceptance.

The light of from the star of the Christmas tree was steady. Jose slowly moved from the bed and asked Maria if she was okay, She nodded. We offered her warm packs for her lower belly, and she accepted then as if they were the greatest of gifts. Another contraction pulled her inward.

Because Maria had a history of bleeding after birth, Anne suggested a heplock to secure access for an IV. It turned out that we would not need one, but Anne is forever vigilant, for which I am grateful, and Maria willingly offered her arm anyway.

After the procedure, Maria resumed her kneeling position. Jose tried to avoid falling asleep, so lay next to her and held her hand through every contraction. A weak beam of streetlight crept in through an opening between the curtains. That light and the light from the tree were enough for her. She moaned as she alternated between hands and knees position during the contractions, resting against her bed afterward. She accepted sips of water from us gratefully. She felt hot, like many women in labor, and sweat glistened on her skin in the light, giving a palpable softness to the room, even as the contractions grew longer and stronger.

Anne whispered praise to Maria for her hard work. Maria smiled in thanks. She said little, but even during the contractions, she seemed to express gratitude and disappear into the moment. Suddenly, she smiled and reached her hand down to touch the infant who had emerged. Her son was born into our loving hands.

A little baby, pink and plump, kicked his tiny legs and wiggled his little arms. He cried as his lower chin trembled. She held him close to her breast and he stopped crying and began to root and suckle at her breast. She looked at her baby and adored him; she and Jose wept and smiled simultaneously. She bent down to kiss him on his little head. Jose appeared cautious at first to touch him, but Maria's arms unfolded and she laid the baby on her lap so that Jose could take a look at his son.

The proud new father blushed and stretched his finger out for the infant to grasp. The infant looked at his father, who burst out in tears and laughter. The other children were woken up by the commotion. They came close to greet their younger brother.

When it was nearly daybreak. Maria's mother prepared morning coffee and eggs for Maria. It was truly Christmas morning. We shared an early morning celebration with the family before heading off to our own Christmases.

I lugged my equipment down the stairs and placed it into my trunk. Then I started the engine and turned on the heat. As I pulled away from the curb, I pushed "Play" and Johnny started to sing, *Fall on your knees! Oh, hear the angel voices*. "No one can hit the notes as well as Johnny," I say to myself.

Thanks, Dad, for the memories.

The Divine Ms. M

Two things I have learned in my years as a midwife are: midwives come from unexpected places, and never underestimate the will of a young woman. Pure will is what helped Myrna, a young mother determined to be a midwife find her destiny. Myrna experienced tension between who she was in her world and who she wanted to be. Her father had died when she was thirteen. On his death bed, she had promised him that she would finish school. It provided a strong motivation to be something in her life.

At the age of 15, she became pregnant and still managed to excel academically. She had delivered with the midwives and continued her school work, and still showed an interest in wanting to support other young moms in her position. She was also determined to be a good mom. She carried a breast pump with her to school. She inquired at the clinic about opportunities to volunteer and joined our peer breastfeeding support group. She announced to her guidance counselor that she wanted to be a midwife. The guidance counselor told her that this was not a realistic goal but she could consider becoming a medical assistant. She wanted alternatives, so she someone suggested that she could go into the non-traditional female role of auto mechanic. No one seemed to give her credit for her intelligence or be willing to see any possibilities for a young fifteen-year-old mother in her position.

She had delivered with our midwifery team and had taken my childbirth classes. I had assisted her with breastfeeding postpartum. She had a keen sense of understanding with regard to birth and breastfeeding. Her questions revealed a more than casual interest in the matter. I suggested she should consider being a midwife. Her mother quickly interrupted, "She can't be a midwife; she has too much attitude."

I responded, "Exactly why she needs to be a midwife. We need women with attitude to advocate for others." After that, Myrna began to volunteer as a breastfeeding peer counselor and then as a doula. After graduation, she began nursing studies at the University.

During her second pregnancy, when she was married to Emilio, she began having contractions and called me to alert me that she had mild contractions and had lost her mucus plug. She had an inkling that she would go fast. I, on the other hand, missed the mark and instructed her to call when the contractions were closer together. The contractions picked up that afternoon, and took all her energy. She had a hard time getting to the phone to inform us that she was in heavy labor. When I picked up the phone, it was obvious that she was already in transition. The team sped down to the South Side from our north-side homes. Basia arrived first on the scene to find that Myrna and Emilio had delivered their baby themselves. We had the dubious honor of delivering the placenta and cleaning up after the birth.

Myrna's next child also arrived before the midwives. Her children, like their momma, were not waiting around for someone else and Myrna's confidence in her own ability to do it alone allowed her to deliver unassisted without fear.

Growing up, she acquired wisdom beyond her years. but there was something lacking. She graduated from high school and then entered nursing school, intending to follow the path to her true self. She wanted to learn more about midwifery and began working at the clinic as a doula.

Myrna is part diva, part scholar. She became fond of partying, but realized she was moving away from her dreams. So she surrounded herself with midwives and often sought them out to act as her sounding board as she reflected on her life and efforts to keep her true spirit intact. She went through the stages of early adulthood, but she could wander and then return home. She did become a midwife, learning the craft and how to help women. She has joined the circle. She is able to help women in her community just as women have helped her.

Myrna initially coasted on her intelligence. She gradually moved away from her youthful concerns to a become a strong mother figure and midwife herself. She struggled to improve herself and encourage scholarship in other single mothers. Mentorship can radically change a life.

She went to a typical South Side Chicago school, and was a bright student who read books beyond the prescribed reading list. She graduated top of her class despite carrying a breast pump around.

At 23, she had another baby and needed to come back to her mother's home for a year. Her life took another direction when she decided to continue her studies. She had been married to Emilo for several years and they had two children together. She conceded that the relationship was not best for her or her children, and returned home to her mother.

She realized that to become a midwife, she would need to become more disciplined, and gradually arrived at a sense of purpose that less intense people will never experience. She is not your poster child for teenaged mothers; she is lively and natural, with a wide range of interests. She was a fast-living teenager and a major intellectual. She blossomed in her 20s, learning how to be a single mother and discovering that the pursuit of pleasure can make life more difficult. Gradually, Myrna cultivated a community of friends and mentors.

While she was still in school, she worked as a crisis hot line responder. One semester, out of the blue, she was awarded a private scholarship for single mothers. The scholarship was from the estate of a single mother who had raised children as a nurse. This made all the difference that semester and despite her worries of financial support, Myrna was able to continue her education. She finished her education as a nurse and then pursued her education as a midwife.

Myrna is an example to me of a woman who does not compromise her true nature, and it was her true nature that demonstrated her strength as a midwife. At many points in her life she could have fallen into abyss, but her "attitude" is what compelled her to keep going. She is a single mother, with a home, children in private schools, and a job as a nurse-midwife in a community health center, giving hope to women as women have given hope to her.

Rules are to be Bent and Sometimes Broken

I really liked Linda from the moment I met her. She was not as famous, outgoing, creative, or successful as some of our more colorful clients. She was extremely plain, with long, straight mouse-brown hair hanging limply around her pale, white face. What impressed me was the sense that she was at peace with herself. In fact, she greeted me, "Peace," and she meant it.

She had been born in Philadelphia, the City of Brotherly Love, as the youngest of three children in an upper, middle-class family. Her father was a physician and her mother a nurse who retired once she married. Full of adventurous spirit and seeking new experiences, Linda attended a small liberal arts college in another state. There, she met a young African-American man named Frederick, who felt his role in life was to fight poverty, work for social justice, and reclaim his African roots. She listened to him and never turned back. A follower of Marcus Garvey, whose Universal Negro Improvement Association raised the banner of black pride decades before Frederick was born, he embraced the Rastafarian movement. One of his beliefs was embodied in the following quote from Marcus Garvey:

> *We are moving from one state of organization to another, and we shall continue until we have thoroughly lifted ourselves in the organization of GOVERNMENT.*

Certainly, most midwifery movements can relate to this struggle, as too often midwives have been the target of the rules of government instead of being allowed to govern ourselves. Most laws pertaining to midwives throughout the years were meant to deter the freedom of their practice, and therefore the freedom of women and families. It is often the client who steps out of society's norms, desiring self-determination by seeking the care of a midwife who does home births.

Not long after they met, the couple wed and Frederick began a life-long venture following the ideas of Marcus Garvey and building up the community. The couple also had several children, believing that children were a blessing, much to the consternation of Linda's father. She had married an equally intense man, and providing for the family while funding his work proved a challenge. Linda gave up her inheritance, abandoned her past possessions, and moved to Chicago, making it their permanent residence. The couple felt the move represented freedom.

When I met Linda, she had already gone through a number of challenges. She sometimes spent the day tending to dirty dishes and laundry, and cooked daily for a large family. Frederick was a steady worker who followed his cause after work, often with Linda at his side at the kitchen table. On the outside, it looked like she had thrown away the good life, but the life she chose was to be an outstanding mother and an awesome gardener. She and her husband were willing to fight for something they revered more than the so-called good life. They did not seem to be rebelling against society, but rather had embraced an alternative way of living that reflected who they were and what they believed. Frederick suggested that the real purpose of education was to help people find their true identity. Linda seemed to find her true identity in discovering an uncommon level of contentment in her daily living.

A key aspect of Linda's essence was gratitude. She always gave thanks; she would greet you with a blessing, and bid you peace as you departed. She lived in a permanent state of thanks. She cherished her garden, her children, and her ability to feel blessed. She made me and others feel the center of attention.

She loved the individual person. Once she had accepted a life of poverty, she was free to live a life of love.

I was able to attend two of her three home births. She had ten children in total. The last was her most difficult.

Posterior births can sometimes bring on more back labor and longer pushing stages. We waited in her bedroom—Carrie, my midwife partner on the birth, Linda, and me. Frederick, her husband, was attending to the kids. During the pauses of a longer-than-usual second stage, we chatted, just three women sitting on a bed in the late afternoon. A May breeze blew through the window, which was slightly open. You could smell the soft May flowers from Linda's garden as we talked.

Linda sat there, holding her own with the contractions, occasionally dozing, sometimes engaging us in small talk. At one point, we started talking about her family. She missed them and understood that they would never really accept her or her choices, but still loved them. She also felt that her in-laws had never really accepted them as a biracial couple from different cities, different cultures and different perspectives. Thus, she and Fredrick had little family support for their ten children.

Her story reminded me of my own in-laws. My mother-in-law converted from Presbyterianism to Catholicism, coming from a family of four. My father-in-law was an only child, and then had ten children. I launched into story, which

I believe is an accurate metaphor for the cultural differences between my own family and my husband's family, despite the fact that we both come from large families. It was the way they played croquet!

I was horrified when I discovered that my husband's family played by rules that no other neighborhood played by. They allowed balls to instantly be "poisoned" instead of earning the status of poison, so basically, the joy of playing croquet was to smack the ball of your opponent instead of developing the skill of aiming the ball so that it would pass through a series of hoops. Some of them avoided the hoops altogether. I was still miffed as I told the story, clearly forgetting I was supposed to be giving labor support. Carrie, the other midwife, being her direct self, brought me back to the birth, "Mary, neither of us play croquet, so we don't even know what you're talking about."

Linda smiled and gave me a knowing nod. She seemed to have acquired the wisdom that allows for thinking beyond the "hoops" and the rules of the game. It is a way of thinking that is not arrogant, but that honors the innocence and the not knowing that remains when one forgets about the hoops and the rules. Her son had the same plan.

A typical series of movements for a baby in labor is to descend, move down the pelvis, and then flex its head and internally rotate its heads so that the head is facing downward (if the mother is lying down). Linda's youngest son was finding his own path, and changing the rules of giving birth. He was to be delivered in a posterior position, or "sunny-side up." Often, the occiput (back of the head) can be held up on the sacral promontory and the head can deflex in this position, causing a failure to descend through the pelvis.

We could try to create a stronger contraction, hoping that it leads to descent and rotation to a more favorable position. We could ask her to try getting on her hands and knees, to walk, or to try nipple stimulation, but with Linda's guidance, we did nothing. She accepted that this was just going to be a longer second stage. She waited until her own contractions built up and then, by flexing her own legs and working with her son's forces, created the space for him to move and birth in his own way. Posterior deliveries are rare, but she made it look simple and ordinary.

In truth, there are no rules for how a baby wants to be delivered. There are patterns, but seldom rules. I once heard a story from a midwife working in a small rural hospital about how a new midwife pleaded with her, asking "But what are the rules?" The more experienced midwife simply replied, "There are no rules. You just have to be smarter than everyone else if you want to go practice differently."

In Linda's case, I don't know if she was smarter, but she certainly was kinder than most as she set about changing the rules to practice life as she saw fit. As for her son, he continued to have his own rules and demand more attention than his siblings. He would be her last.

"The last will be first; the meek will inherit the earth."

The following two stories illuminate the meaning of the above verse, paraphrased from Matthew 5:5.

Dina was a mother of three living in a shelter. I was her home visitor, offering her breastfeeding support and a link to the clinic. On my first day, I approached the shelter, rang the bell, and uncertainly climbed the steps when I was buzzed in. The first floor was a huge room where single men were camping, literally camping, with blankets strung as tents akin to what we did as children to create separate spaces.

The second floor, I was told, was the family unit. The receptionist sent me to Dina's room. I had met Dina once, before she had left the hospital. She was recently homeless. Her husband had lost his job in her seventh month of pregnancy, and she was unemployed at the time. They had four children and neither came from stable families. No one had enough room to take in a family of six. She had a job babysitting that would start in a month. For the time being, a shelter room would be their home.

The shelter space had a sweaty smell, like a men's locker room. Dina greeted me and behind her, I saw bunk beds and suitcases, neatly crammed into a room no bigger than a storage locker. She nursed as we chatted. She had concocted breast support for her enlarged, lactating breasts using the cord from her bathrobe. I mentioned to her that the primary midwife was concerned that she might be depressed.

"Depressed?" she seemed surprised. "Mary, my life might not be ideal, but I don't think I'm depressed."

She had no interest in anti-depressants to get her through her post-partum. "You know what would make me feel much better? A good-fitting bra."

I went to the local department store and brought her a bra.

Sometimes we need to ask people what they need instead of assuming we already know.

Millie the Meek

Millie had so few resources, life skills, and luck that she invoked a response from a whole village of midwives, community members, and friends to both assist and seek justice.

Millie did not believe life should happen as you wish, but that life happened as it does. To most, her life would be considered intolerable. There seemed to be no reason behind what was going on. While I often feel safe in the knowledge that all things happen for a reason, the situation with Millie did not fit into my view of things. Even after all my years as a midwife, I didn't understand why I would be on this birth, with this woman who never struggled with her life, but instead maintained a quiet acknowledgement of her dismal fate. My efforts felt futile in her presence, and I had no idea how to help her.

Millie did not know how to read or write. She seemed be eternally content, she smiled often, but didn't need to make sense of the world or the workings of a busy Chicago life. She didn't know the difference between the faucet's hot or cold nozzles. She couldn't operate a telephone. She couldn't read the street signs and didn't know how to count out money for bus fare. But rather than cause her unhappiness, these handicaps reinforced to her that some things are in our power, others are not. She felt she had little control over how life would unfold, and yet, she avoided the usual anxiety that comes with poverty and disease.

My friend and former client Inez came to my home and pleaded with me to find work for Millie, who recently arrived from, "an island near Puerto Rico," as Millie explained (known to most of us as the Dominican Republic). She had come to be with her husband who was "guapo," she said with a fling of her hand to suggest that he was gay. She seemed to accept this, too, as well as his work as a prostitute, which we would learn about later.

I found work for her in my own home. She had to learn how to use both hot and cold water when she bathed my daughter. She slowly learned to use the phone, but because she feared writing messages she would tell my friends and family when they called that I was taking a shower. For a while, my friends thought I had peculiar hygiene habits.

It turned out that Millie was eight or nine months pregnant, which she herself did not know. She was rather tall and had a large frame, so I am embarrassed to admit that none of us figured out just how far along she was. We helped her get set up with prenatal care and conducted the necessary lab work. She tested positive for syphilis.

Soon after we began her treatment, her membranes ruptured and she went into labor. To be more specific, her membranes ruptured on my sofa when I wasn't home. My husband found himself beginning labor support and cleaning up the sofa as part of his duties of being a husband of a midwife. I once bought him a bumper sticker that read "Real men support midwives." He had inserted the word "foolish" between *real* and *men*. This might have been one of those moment he felt, "Why me?" He paged me and when I returned the call, he informed me what had occurred.

She had no car and they could not reach her family. I hurried home and immediately brought her to the hospital. One of our amazing back-up physicians had accepted her into his care. I was alone with her in labor; her husband was absent during the birth.

She was stoic through most of it, accepting pain as part of the process. Throughout the labor, her mother-in-law called to speak with me. She stated she had gotten in touch with Millie's husband, but that he was too busy to come. She kept asking me to stay until he could arrive. Her final call was about an hour before Millie would birth her son.

The mother-in-law informed me she had once again reached Millie's husband, but he was not interested in coming. "Don't let her know this. Tell her that he was called to work, something."

Millie actually didn't inquire about what her mother-in-law said and didn't want to know. I simply said, "She said he is not yet coming." She accepted this, But she was not ready to accept or see, at the time of birth, her infant who was covered with syphilis sores.

Immediately the tone of the room changed, and instead of a joyous reception, everyone acted as if the plague had arrived. The baby was taken to the special care nursery, and Dr. Barnes, our back-up, and I stayed to assist Millie with recovery. I was alerted that her husband had arrived, and when I went out to meet him, to my surprise, he had brought a male partner with him. He was dressed as if auditioning for the movie, *Saturday Night Fever*, in a billowy blouse and tight pants. He told me he had no intention of staying; he just wanted to see his new son.

His partner spoke English. "How is the mother?"

I felt as if I had entered the theater of the absurd. I escorted her husband to see her and told him he was to stay with her. Miraculously, Millie was delighted to see him. He again asked me to stay in his place, but I refused. Millie also insisted that he stay, the first time I heard any firmness in her voice. He sheepishly sat in the chair. I returned to the waiting area and informed his guest that Millie's husband would be staying for a while.

Sarah, one of my midwife colleagues, returned the next day. The nurses were still mumbling; no one wanted to touch "the syphilis baby." With just one look at Millie's sad and embarrassed face, Sarah knew the nurses' judgment had gotten to her. For the first time since we knew her, Millie was ashamed. Sarah brought her to the nursery with Dr. Barnes' permission. The nurse left them the alone with baby. Millie turned away and began to cry.

Sarah encouraged her to hold her baby and went to the crib where her baby lay. As she reached for the gloves to protect herself, she caught Millie's eye and put the gloves down. Millie did not need to see another person reject this child. In an act of pure love, Sarah scooped up the diseased child with her bare hands.

With Sarah's encouragement, Millie began to bond with her child. In time, her son recovered, and so did Millie. She decided to leave her husband, and earned just enough money to buy a return ticket back home.

Sarah's generosity with Millie and her baby reminds me that maybe it isn't the actual events in a mother's life that are so terrible, but the interpretation we give to them. Witnessing such an act of courage and risk is one of those moments that causes me to pause before I give judgment on my fellow birth provider. Perhaps in any given moment in time, we are called to do the right thing for that moment. The moment can call forth the right action.

In the Company of Women

The cloudy spring day threatened rain. Shoshana began the morning by gazing out the window and stroking her belly as light waves of contractions came and went. She had imagined this day for so long and now it was here. Nearby, her mother folded clothes, smiling slightly nervously at her pregnant daughter.

The bond between mother and daughter had always been strong. They had moved so often together through the years that their interdependence was almost too powerful. In fact, Shoshana had quarreled with her mother throughout the pregnancy. Her mother would often visit unannounced and bring unsolicited advice.

They were Russian-Jewish immigrants who had moved to Chicago in the late 80s and 90s following the collapse of the Soviet Union. They had come to

Chicago after living briefly in both South Africa and Israel, each move an attempt to escape anti-Semitism. They had come in search of a better life and freedom.

Shoshana had chosen a home birth against her mother's wishes. Shoshana had told us during her prenatal care that she sought birth as a rite of passage. Part of the passage was a desire to settle her life of wandering by establishing a place to call home.

As labor slowly progressed, Shoshana called her husband George, a native Chicagoan, to come home from work. By mid-afternoon, she had called our midwifery team, announcing that her contractions had progressed to every 3 to 5 minutes, lasting over a minute with little rest in between. She thought it best to have us nearby. As we arrived, she greeted us, but then let us make ourselves at home so that she could go about being a laboring woman without needing to play hostess.

An hour passed, and her younger sister Rachal arrived. Shortly afterward, her mother called in a few "aunts"—best friends from her past who also lived in Chicago, creating a support team of four women and two midwives. George seemed comfortable with the abundance of women. He nodded at each as they arrived.

On a dresser near where Shoshana labored, I noticed a framed photograph of a much younger Shoshana, surrounded by her mother and several of the other women in the room. Now these grown women surrounded Shoshana again, awaiting the arrival of her child. That is one of the more beautiful aspects of the labor journey—the original contract between mother and daughter expanding into a new context. Birth and end-of-life passages seem to offer insights about our larger purpose within our family and village.

When I first arrived, I felt as if I was entering a sacred space. I walked toward the circle. Four women from her past, the wise women, the sister, and the midwives sat drawn into a circle. A blanket was wrapped around Shoshana. Someone brushed her hair. Her belly was bathed with warm cloths. Each woman had brought a gift and words of encouragement. They seemed to all breathe in unison.

The labor pains became more intense. As Shoshana began whimpering that she couldn't take it anymore, the women formed a chorus. "Yes, you can. Keep going. You can do it." Many there did not understand why Shoshana would choose a home birth in contrast to the modern hospital suite, but they understood that she could freely choose her way of birthing the next generation.

A few hours later, Shoshana knelt over the end of the bed, squatting, held up by her husband.

Her mother began praying softly between contractions as Shoshana tried to rest. Shoshana was not religious and had been brought up in a fairly secular fashion in the Soviet Union.

She had told us during her prenatal care that she sought birth as a rite of passage, and that she was at home in her place of her inner wisdom. She understood that her home represented a safe haven. She was a home for her unborn daughter and she kept a safe haven for her daughter's journey to a new home within her arms.

Shoshana briefly drifted to sleep, aware of her companions, but safe within the circle, cocooned in a blanket with only a foot sticking out into the cool, quiet morning air. She curled with the contractions and stretched her leg after each one. Her sister bent down to offer Shoshanna a sip of water. She seemed in awe of her sister—her youth and lack of a partner making it difficult for her to imagine that some day she might also share in this ancient ritual of giving birth.

As Shoshana moved through the point of birth where the fear of disappointing another melts away and a woman claims her inner self, the women and the midwives kept the space to allow for the vulnerability to deepen. There were moments of tears and moments of joy between contractions when Shoshana looked at her audience as they greeted her with smiles, cool cloths for her forehead, and sips of tea.

She pushed for an hour, rather short for a first time mother. She squatted throughout the pushing stage, her husband sitting behind her so that she could rest between contractions. The women chose to kneel and lean against each other to catch a glimpse of the infant's emerging head.

Shortly, the infant arrived. Home. Home in this apartment made sacred by the love and support within. Home within her mother's soothing arms. Home within the circle of loving women who would continue to nurture both mother and child.

The Good Woman

mma Jean's backyard was full of hanging laundry and kids playing in the grass. I was eating lunch at her picnic table on one of my pre-natal home visits, a common and practical habit for home birth midwives. These casual visits allow us to see our mothers in their homes, on their own turfs, and also served as a dry run in case we needed to find the house in the middle of the night.

Emma Jean is one of the many good women of the earth who birth every day, every hour, and everywhere. She knew her marriage to be safe and secure. Ed, her husband, would always be there for her.

She looked forward to her birth, a day in which they would take a break from Little League games, cookouts, cars that needed to be fixed, and laundry that needed to be folded. She wanted a natural childbirth because it seemed like the safest way to deliver a baby—no drugs. It also seemed like the best way to welcome this new baby into her family.

Emma Jean's previous births, for one reason or another, needed some intervention and seemed to lack a personal touch that she desired. She had delivered her first child when she was younger, and she didn't know much about the birth process. It was a typical hospital birth. She considered her current relationship with that daughter, who was now approaching her own adulthood. The struggles with breastfeeding and becoming a mom, which she approached with stubbornness and Midwestern perseverance, caused Emma Jean to think that she might have started off easier had she had better support in the hospital with her first daughter's birth.

At her next birth she delivered twins. They were slightly premature and some mild complications occurred, so they were whisked away at the moment of birth. They were in the intensive care unit for over a week. Again, she persevered, nursing them to health and doing what she had to do. She remembered being frightened about their fragile lungs and small size. She stayed at the hospital all day and pumped at night to make sure they were receiving only breast milk. That felt like a long recovery, but her hard work paid off, and they were now healthy four year olds.

It was a nice summer day, and the breeze murmured through the trees as we sipped lemonade. "Mary," she remarked, "I'm just hoping for one good birth in my life. I hope this will be it." She had had no complications with this pregnancy, and no indications that she would have preterm labor. It was very possible her wish would come true.

She went into labor in early autumn. The morning fog had settled densely. I could barely see to drive so I proceeded slowly, afraid I might hit a deer darting from the prairie grass that lined both sides of the road. Yellow and reddish hues streaked the sky, and a blinding glare blasted through my windshield. I love fall in the Midwest, despite the challenge of driving to country births through wind gusts and fog. Some of the joy of doing home births is my chance to step into the journey again each time. Even the process of engaging with nature just to safely navigate the road is sacred.

Ed, Emma Jean's husband, had the coffee brewing. Kathy, her best friend, prepared the warm cloths for comfort and relief, and her mom kept on eye on the four-year-olds, who were still asleep. Emma Jean's eldest daughter, Samantha, sat across from her mother in a recliner. She seemed a tad shy and uncertain about how to fit in. As Emma Jean began to rock in heavy labor, Samantha rushed to her side to hold her hand without another thought. Everyone in the family seemed to want a good birth for Emma Jean.

Emma Jean opted for the shower and let the hot water pummel her back to beat away the pain. She absently watched water run down the drain for nearly an hour. And then suddenly, she needed to get out. After a quick toweling off, she returned to her bedroom for the next contraction. She tried to steady her breath, and gripped Kathy and Samatha's hands as Ed applied pressure to her lower back. When the contraction passed, she sipped water calmly and waited for the next.

When her body began to shake, she leaned forward and grabbed for Ed's arm. Her knuckles were white with each strong contraction. *"OW, OW,"* she yelped. Ed endured the knuckle clench silently. We kept the warm cloths coming, and he placed them on her back. Her eyes closed. We gathered her hair into a ponytail and wiped sweat from her face with a cool cloth. She entered a cycle: being seized by contraction, releasing herself from its grip, napping for a moment, and then starting again. We witnessed her desperation for each contraction to come to an end, her simultaneous state of feeling out of her mind, and yet understanding that she needed special courage to do this.

Her cheeks looked red, her eyes were excited, her lips dry, as sweat beads lined up above her upper lip. We reminded her to catch some rest between the contractions. She nodded, deep in thought despite so much commotion.

Between each contraction, she slept. Endorphins had given her the gift of dreams, a momentary oasis. Then the deep guttural sounds came. She began pushing. She began to pant, yell, pant, and yell. Her baby's head crowned, and I knew then that today would be special; at last, a good birth for a good woman.

Afterwards, she lay cuddling her newborn, nestled by her family and friends, floating in a state of gratitude.

It was rainy when I drove home, misty rain that illuminated maroon and golden meadows. I called home to check on the kids. I too would be returning to my life of Little League games, homework, and dirty dishes. On that drive, I once again knew that my life of a midwife is about being an ordinary woman who witnesses everyday miracles.

Birth is as Fair as Life Gets

Sally was the type of person whose expectations are just a little too high. At 12, Sally imagined her adult life as a writer would be a clear path if she simply worked hard. At 24, she expected to move out west within six months (it took seven years). She was also certain that the balanced spiritual life she found at age 30 would last. Even though it's natural to miscalculate, these little failures devastated her in that "how-can-I-even-go-on" way that becomes really silly after age 35.

For some reason, adapting to life's errors eluded me, though Sally now knows it to be destructive. Each supposed failure carved a deeper groove in her soul that flared and attacked every time she attempted to explain what had gone wrong. She gave herself a *schpiel*— "Yes, you followed your gut, did your research, worked your hardest, but sometimes things just don't work out."

And yet, when it came time to trust in her birth plan, she was still under the impression that she had complete control over her life. When I was a younger midwife, I often felt the same; if we do our best and work our hardest, things will work out. While this can be true for some moments in our life, it isn't always the case. The hard lessons that wisdom requires can make us all feel like failures. Life isn't about failing, however, as much as it is about getting back up.

Almost immediately upon conceiving, Sally's expectations went rogue again. The ambitious, yet sabotaging belief that she could bear her child the "right" way fixed itself in her 36-year-old head. Nevertheless, given her previous experiences, she should not have been surprised when the birth did not go as she expected—but she was. And because of her background, it has taken her almost three years to acknowledge that medically saving her baby and herself was not a failure of will, or the death of who she thought she was. On the contrary, it was an incredible chance for rebirth.

Just to be clear, there were real medical signs that her birth plan would come to pass as she wished. She had gotten pregnant on the first try—these days, a stroke of luck for a woman over 35. She had chosen my birth class that promotes natural childbirth and a hospital in a liberal town with a famously experienced practice of midwives. She rarely felt sick during pregnancy, had fulfilling ultrasounds, and everything tested positive. She had a caring and supportive birth partner who came to my prenatal appointments, asked real questions, and then wrote down the answers. She had gained a good amount of weight and was proud of it, allowing her body to determine a size for itself instead of obsessing about each pound gained. This, along with her lively yoga practice full of headstands and backbends, which she performed up until nearly the end of her term, was exactly the vision of pregnancy she wanted. Liberated. Wild. Natural.

Then there was the sign from above. When she was five months pregnant and vacationing in Costa Rica, Sally caught a rare glimpse of a giant sea turtle giving birth on a beach at midnight. The sacredness of the creature and her labor was obvious to Sally though she was part of a crowd of a dozen observers and field interns scurrying around to collect the eggs for safer development. Even so, the message was clear: life was primal, and birth itself was a force of nature. She would deliver majestically like this enormous prehistoric creature, because that was how birth was meant to happen.

Fast forward four months. The first night of Sally's labor seemed like a cosmic confirmation. An unbelievable electrical storm seized the outside world while she and her husband breathed though ten straight hours of contractions. As the wind howled menacingly, she was surprised by how completely manageable the pain was. She popped in *Eternal Om*, an amazing, transcendent disc of chanting that she later could not listen to again. The pain came first at ten, then seven, then four, then two minutes apart. Two minutes apart, she knew from her research, was a good sign. The baby would come by morning.

At five a.m., things simmered down, and she half expected that this was the still before the storm where she was supposed to start pushing. But when I told her she was only 2 centimeters dilated, a voice from within said, wrong again. Sally swallowed the night's exhaustion and prepared for another, harder day of labor. "That's fine," she thought defiantly, "there's still time to do this right."

The contractions continued every 15 to 20 minutes through Wednesday, and into Wednesday night. By Thursday, they were getting farther apart. By Thursday night, she had maybe one per hour. On Friday, she was utterly confused. She was doing everything right. Where was her birth? She and her partner reluctantly went to the doctor in a bleary, but bemused state. She expected little in the way of medical help; it was a natural childbirth after all. "What else can they do but tell me to wait?" she thought.

Sally certainly respected doctors, but considered their role in her life unnecessary. Of course, she had always received required medical treatment, and that was true for her pregnancy, too. But for most of her life, even taking an aspirin for a headache or menstrual cramps was rare. She partially tore a rotator cuff and rehabbed it herself. She learned to balance depression and anxiety with plenty of yoga and meditation. Doctors, in her life as well as in her vision of her birth, would be a formality.

The surgeon of the practice felt differently. The midwives almost apologized to me when they cited his reasoning. "You're two weeks late, over thirty five, and already 72 hours into labor. You need to go to the hospital."

I tried to help her see things optimistically. A little Pitocin—the synthetic contraction hormone—could help. It was still possible, maybe even more than possible, for her to birth vaginally with perhaps some further intervention. She reserved the room with the big birthing tub. She brought her favorite essential oils. On Saturday morning, the attending nurse fastened the IV to her arm and said, "We'll have this baby out by 5 p.m."

It did not happen that way. Sally will never forget the concerned look on the primary midwife's face as the baby's heart tones dropped while the Pitocin forced contractions every two minutes for 14 more hours, as the water bag revealed bacteria when it was artificially broken.

The pain was no longer manageable. She was now 85 hours and three interventions deep into this birth and still hoping for the natural result, despite the wires attached to her cervix and coming out of her vagina. The hospital became her new sterile and mathematical universe, where it seemed she would wait and wonder forever.

It had been determined at some point that the baby was posterior (which I usually believe is exaggerated in most suspensions of this), or "sunny-side up," and having difficulty moving toward the birth canal. She complained of pain in odd places: her buttocks, her thighs, but not the lower part of her abdomen where pain is most typical.

By midnight, it was suggested that she be given an epidural so she could sleep. Even after a full day on Pitocin, Sally had been stuck at 9cm for the past several hours. Thick meconium was expelled when the bag had broken several hours previously. (This is the baby's first stool, which is sometimes released when under stress. The baby's heart beat would only tolerate a position of her on her back. She seemed to progress in labor with other positions but the heart rate would plummet with each attempt.

By that time, Sally had been crying and dry heaving for hours. She had already drenched herself and everyone from sitting in the tub and showering under warm water, hoping to flush some activity into the situation.

"Let's do it," her husband said at the recommendation of an epidural. As her doula and friend, I could see that the labor pattern was dysfunctional and the pain was not that of usual labor, but rather that brought on by ineffective contractions. Sometimes, these labors can be helped by epidurals, rest, and the passing of time. When the shot went into her back, it was a different kind of pain, not so much of physical discomfort, but from the feeling of having failed.

These are such tough births when the woman wants to do it naturally, but all roads lead elsewhere. I consider women who experience these kinds of births akin to Moses. He was so close to the Promised Land that it was in his view, but he was not allowed to enter it. Yet the children of Israel safely passed into the Promised Land, just as Sally's child did. God had other plans. I don't often think Pitocin or epidurals are the answer, but when birth proceeds in certain patterns of dysfunction, you use the tools at hand.

For Sally, the experience of failing her own expectations always held the "salt in the wound" feeling of public humiliation. Even though no one was ever really around to watch her fail, an innate sense of shame followed her for not being able to fulfill one assignment or another. The shame has never stopped her from trying, but on that night, as she slept the slumber of the drugged, she thought about how many times during the last three days she had wanted to quit and run away and just start the birth over again at some other time. How humiliated she was at once again not being able to succeed at something she imagined for herself. At the same time, she tried to balance this feeling within the context of the new life awaiting her help.

She awoke to find the surgeon, a middle-aged Lebanese man, wearing a collared shirt and tie under a white hospital jacket. Although it was six in the morning on a Sunday, her former enemy had taken the time to dress up, shave, and present a face of calm that restored in her a dignity she thought she'd never feel again. He waited for her to speak first.

"I think something's wrong," she whispered. "Take her out."

She tells me now she doesn't' know why she said 'her' suddenly, since throughout the whole pregnancy, she had been certain she was carrying a boy. Another miscalculation. Within 45 minutes, she had gone from being alone in her struggle with the death of her soul, to being in a hospital television drama where interns were cracking jokes in their green scrubs. Nothing, not the bright lights, nor the weirdness of having her lower abdomen shaved and cut open by a team of young medical students, seemed to bother her.

The testimonies of women who have natural childbirths gush about the euphoria they feel from the hormones that douse the agony of those last few pushes. She, too, had been looking forward to this euphoria. But before she had a chance to lament this failure, she was swept away by an entirely different feeling.

As she wheeled into surgery on a clean, white sheeted gurney, she was absolutely thrilled that her 90 hours of labor were coming to an end, and that someone—in fact a whole team of people—was going to help take this child out of her body. When she saw the long white arms and legs of her writhing, screaming baby girl over the curtain, a flush of relief lifted her to a sacred place.

Once she got out of the hospital and jumped into mothering, she did her best to ignore the remaining hesitation. Though she intellectually knew her choices had been correct, she suffered a relapse in her perspective about the birth. For her first 18 months of motherhood, she retold the story to many women who, because their natural childbirth had gone well, had surprisingly little empathy. Somehow, the sense that she had suffered a misfortune stayed with her, even while she was nursing and caring for a glorious baby girl.

She had the strange feeling that she was being judged by other mothers and believed that they, too, saw her C-section as a failure, or if not that, then a triumph for them. Even now, when she reads literature about the glories of natural childbirth or water births or home births, she occasionally get a whiff of that misplaced righteousness.

Birth, like life, doesn't always deal a fair hand. The woman who smokes a pack of cigarettes a day and could care less about a natural birth, sometimes slips a healthy baby out without pain, while women like Sally, who desire a better outcome, aren't granted their wish.

My thoughts on this are many. It's probable that the cigarette mom was given a lot other raw deals, which made her smoke cigarettes, and birth happens to be the place that life gave her a break. It's also common in my experience that women after C-sections feel very much like Sally. Something physically, mentally, and emotionally feels "off." The stars don't feel aligned and this feeling can linger.

It can be a birth, especially a vaginal birth, that can put this in perspective. In our grandmothers' generation, it was usually the first birth, if there was to be a birth, that was hard, not as safe, and often one birth among many. Today, women have fewer births so the context has changed, and so a woman's perspective of her birth and a role as a mother can be all encompassing.

Sally took my C-Section lesson to heart and sought medical help for the malady of the mind. Post-partum depression, when combined with a life of unacknowledged depression, can be paralyzing. She said "no" to medications and had a hundred excuses: she was nursing, it was winter, she wanted to lose some weight first, she didn't want to be a zombie. Then she looked in the mirror one morning and saw, behind dark eyes and a vacant stare, that she already was.

The pill was small and blue in her hand. The result of swallowing it was undeniably positive. She felt better, healthier, and actually content within five minutes of swallowing it. In the same way that she at first resisted, and then surrendered to, a non-natural childbirth, she had now found great relief in surrendering to the reality that we all sometimes need help. The benefit, beside the fact that her daughter gets to have a mother who isn't obsessed with failure, is that she actually excited to live in a world where failures are part of the deal, and where the business of living every day for what it is, expectations aside, can deliver a sweet and unpredictable reward.

Sally continues to reflect, to do yoga, to create space in her life for growth. The blue pill is not her only solution. Life can continue to throw her challenges, but like the birth of her child, when all paths seemed to be blocked, we use the resources we have on hand.

The Blessed Mother Mary

The experience between midwife and mother is shared, though their roles are vastly different. The role of the midwife, as was the role of ancient healers or medicine women, is to maintain a tranquil and healing environment for the mother. The midwife's gift is the ability to maintain a stable reality without being possessed by the mother's birth process. Though she can never truly experience the mother's extraordinary and personal connection to the life force, it is the midwife's job is to nurture it in whatever form it presents itself: a premature birth, a full-term birth, a complicated birth, or even a still birth.

Many pregnant mothers worry about their baby's health. The fear of a stillbirth, or fetal demise, is common, and often continues to plague mothers even after their child is born, grown through infancy, childhood, adolescence and—from what I understand from my late grandmother, who lost an adult son—even into adulthood.

Statistically, fetal demise is rare. I have only witnessed a few fetal demises in my long career as a midwife. I share these following stories not to invoke fear, but rather to honor these souls who have taught me so much about the nature of birth and death. Through these women, I have learned why the precarious nature of life is precisely what makes birth so sacred and women so courageous.

Cora—Grace Revealed

The first day I met Cora, a young woman dressed whimsically in a long blouse and ankle bracelet, I didn't know she would change the course of my midwifery career. During my first summer teaching at the community clinic, Cora requested childbirth classes at home because of a conflict with her aqua-natal exercise class. I agreed, because she had a earnest flare about her and I have a hard time turning down any request that comes with sincerity. I would soon find her insight into maternal child programs, midwifery, motherhood and breastfeeding transforming.

I visited Cora at home for basic instructions and she taught me as much about "a woman's way of knowing" as I did her about pre-natal care. We had had similar lives—both of us came from a large, close-knit families, both of us were willing to take action, and make an effort without worrying about the reward. Though raised Catholic, Cora was also attracted to goddess spirituality, and both helped her find deep power within when she needed it.

Siena was born on a warm summer night. She came into the world surrounded by midwives and Cora's sisters in attendance. She was absolutely perfect in every way, except for a myelomeningocele on her lower spine, a birth defect in which the backbone and spinal canal do not close before birth. The condition is a type of spina bifida. The myelomeningocele required immediate focus and prompt surgery early on in the post-partum period. In the days before the operation, Cora found the power within herself to breastfeed her child and to follow through on every possible resource. Her strength and sense of responsibility allowed her to nurse even after surgery, which was difficult due to position problems. Mothers of babies with spina bifida must work extra diligently to support their child's body and head position. When Siena was finally sent home, Cora learned how to do dressing changes and observe her infant for urological and orthopedic status.

At the time, I served as a co-director of the midwifery services and coordinated education and breastfeeding support to women in the Mexican community, and sought out other committed mothers who had successfully breastfed, to help me assist. Women with special qualities of courage, I believed, would be acknowledged as leaders among their peers and thus help new mothers reconnect with the benefits of breastfeeding. Culturally, bottle feeding propaganda was eroding women's confidence in breastfeeding, and I needed strong women who embraced their inner wisdom regardless of outer fads. Cora was an ideal candidate.

Cora had worked in the program for several years, rising through the ranks from a doula, to a labor support specialist, and eventually a childbirth educator. Key to her success was her ability to build relationships with other women and show them their own capabilities, despite negative messages and sometimes lack of family support. Everyone loved her: new immigrants, teenage mothers, single mothers, homeless mothers. Because of her, our core group of home visiting nurses and midwives expanded to include a dozen breastfeeding counselors, seven paid doulas, childbirth educators, and staff members from the community. We served over 1,200 women a year and performed over 5,000 home visits annually. It was a new model of a maternity program, born of my partnership with Cora. She had a gift for bringing women together and for showing them that the source of grace comes from within.

It was during this time that Cora was pregnant again and going to a private community midwifery practice that I had co-founded. During her check-up with her second baby, the midwife was having difficulty determining the position of the baby and her measurements were inconsistent with the number of weeks of pregnancy. Cora was sent for an ultrasound. During the visit, the baby was shown to have anencephaly, a congenital birth defect that occurs in approximately one in one thousand pregnancies. It is a neural tube defect, just as is spina bifida. Life expectancy for a baby with anencephaly after birth is just a few hours, sometimes a few days at most. Cora decided to be induced and deliver the baby early. She requested that her husband, her sister, and I support her in the labor.

The contractions were initially slow, and while the nursing staff seemed removed, they kept their distance in early labor. They offered her pain medication, which Cora accepted. She dozed off to sleep while waiting for stronger contractions to ensue. They came in the middle of the night. Within a short time, the hour of birth had arrived and her tiny daughter Ana's arrival was imminent. The medical attendants entered the room, among them, the nervous resident who would perform the delivery.

Cora had been on her back, still drowsy from the medication and twisted in her hospital gown, but sat up once the strong contractions came, and pushed. Tiny Ana gave a cry upon arrival, which surprised the resident. He assumed the infant would not be born alive, and, because of his inexperience and devotion to protocol, continued on auto-pilot as if he held a stillborn. He reached for the cold metal bowl, held out by a straight-faced nurse, ready to dispose of the tender, breathing body. Cora's husband, sister, and I gasped in disbelief. His eyes caught the shock in our eyes. He recoiled and thankfully paused, his body stiffened. He looked at the child in his hands, and realized the shocking mistake he had been about to make.

It is easy to be cynical about the resident, but I once had a similar moment of horror in which I participated in a fatality due to auto-pilot. In my early twenties, I had worked in the ER as a crisis worker, when a young boy with sickle cell anemia was brought in. His mother had a difficult time dealing with his sickness and had slapped him, leaving a red mark on his face. Her fear of authorities caused her to delay taking him in for his current crisis.

Wrought with shame, she immediately confessed her violent action when she entered the ER. She was also anxious about his condition. She was placed in a different room and questioned about her violent actions; the young boy was interviewed as well. No one expected the boy to go into cardiac arrest, so he lay alone on a hospital cart, without his mother, whom he kept asking for, and died alone.

His mother was later brought up on manslaughter charges. When she was told of his death, she fell to her knees; the wails of pain, shame, and sorrow still echo in my ears. Few of the staff felt sorry, so caught up in their own ability to step into grief, that they failed to see hers.

The boy's father came in later, complaining about her inability to care for her children. He was probably right. She would likely be in over her head with one child, let alone being a single mother with three children, one of whom was severely ill. So, where was society when she needed aid? Where was this man when she needed help with their child, with his death, with the manslaughter charges, and the shame would trail her the rest of the days of her life? The human condition can be harsh. It is compassion that brings us back to the best humanity can offer.

I still see the vision of the little boy, lying listless on the hospital cot, cracked lips from dehydration, waiting for an IV, waiting for his mother, asking for his mother, while I and the rest of the medical personnel were caught up in the interview protocol. We failed to take the correct action.

It was the memory of the boy that gave me compassion for the young resident during Cora's birth. I was glad he stopped his actions before it was too late.

Cora, still in somewhat of an altered state, sat up to hold her newborn. She gave her young daughter a kiss of peace and held her while her heart still beat. After a few minutes, her child's heart stopped and she lay still.

Preoccupation with protocol gets in the way of relationships, of life. Fortunately, grace exists and it wakes us up in the nick of time. I saw the young boy's death in the ER as a call from God to pay attention to what was important. I also believe redemption comes to us who care to make right our wrongs. A second chance came with tiny Ana's last few breaths in her mother's arms.

Cora arranged a funeral. She adopted a son. She has been a wonderful role model for Siena, a fiercely independent young woman, a good student, and a good swimmer. She recently danced at her Quinceanera and looked spectacular. Cora planned the event, and sat surrounded by her sisters, her former colleagues who were community doulas and childbirth educators, and me. Siena danced beautifully that night, and Cora beamed.

Jenny Smith 1 & 2

My first experience of fetal demise came early on in my career. I was working as a midwife in a large physician practice, and had begun to see Jenny regularly when she was just a few weeks pregnant. She cried at every visit. Though it was early in her pregnancy, she had confided in me that she knew she would probably never see her baby alive. She felt it was her karma for a previous abortion. I was shocked and, too young and inexperienced to respond appropriately. I stammered, protested, and insisted that she shouldn't feel that way.

"Each pregnancy is unique," I said.

She patted my shoulder. "I'm okay. I just needed to tell someone".

She stopped coming on the days I worked at the clinic and began seeing a different midwife and physician. She knew I was too young to commiserate, too idealistic to listen. At 37 weeks gestation, her baby stopped moving. The cause of death, in spite of an autopsy, was unknown. I remembered her premonition.

* * *

Several years later, I had my own practice with another midwife and we had a patient—another Jenny. She was a former smoker but had quit for nearly a decade, and currently enjoyed a healthy lifestyle, eating properly and exercising regularly. Despite her good physical health, she was outwardly anxious and quite upfront about her concerns about having a healthy baby. She feared her prior health choices would come back to haunt her. Though complications were highly unlikely, we agreed that she should have a hospital birth in addition to our labor support. That way, if she encountered any complications, emergency care would be at her fingertips.

Jenny had a normal, healthy pregnancy. She prudently followed a conscientious diet. She exercised moderately. She had a supportive husband. But she cried at every appointment. A week after her due date, she felt light cramping and no fetal movement. While we scanned her belly with a Doppler in search of heart tones, only scratchy sounds echoed back. Our back-up doctor arrived quickly at the hospital, and an ultrasound confirmed the worst. The baby had inexplicably died at 41 weeks.

Jenny's eyes grew large, then darted and flicked around the room as she processed the news. I initially said nothing, but when I felt her grip my hand, I held it. Time had stopped. There was nothing I could say to take away the pain, no gesture to offer that would remove the present reality. I waited, she waited, and then we moved in silence to the labor unit.

Her voice was barely audible as she asked me questions about inducing her labor. I offered to stay with her and her husband, an offer she gratefully accepted. A great heaviness settled into the hospital room that night. Death lurked in the dim hospital room. As if the moment wasn't horrible enough, the attendant nurse rushed in and announced that it was her last night as a labor and delivery nurse before she would retire after 23 years. "I don't want this to be a hard shift," she threatened.

The nurse suggested that Jenny take pain medications. Doing so would help her avoid both the pain of birth and perhaps the memory of the labor. Jenny declined, and the nurse felt rebuked. She began to taunt her.

"Look at you" she scorned, "you are not handling this well." She threatened more routines if Jenny would not agree to the medication. Jenny lowered her head and without speaking, shook her head "no." Her husband and I requested that Jenny be able to labor in peace. The nurse left the room in a huff.

The birth came not long afterward. We occasionally offered water, heat packs, a hand to grip. She sat semi-reclined on the bed and mustered the courage to face the inevitable birth of her dead infant. Her husband and I kept vigil, wiping her forehead, gently wiping a few tears. She was calm and sad. We moved around her in silence, rarely leaving her side. She would nod off to sleep between contractions. During those times, I listened to her moans and held her hand and prayed for the grace to bear the deep loneliness and imminent loss.

She had labored quietly but as the birth grew nearer, she began to reflect on her own life, the life of the baby, and on life's ultimate meaning. Her husband entered the existential cocoon in the next hours that passed, and together, the mourning parents inhabited that intimate space. They talked about how they had already been loving the baby since the moment they knew it was conceived. They talked about how the baby had died in a cradle of love.

No hospital attendants were there to witness when she began to push. We could see her infant's pale blue head emerge, and finally the whole, motionless body. For a moment, no one spoke; the newborn lay still next to Jenny in the hospital bed. She looked like an angel, lips slightly parted, her delicate eyes and lashes closed as if in slumber. Jenny stroked her lifeless body and then brought her close to her chest. She began to rock to and fro with her daughter in her arms. A single cry from her throat gave way to sobs. She leaned against her husband and he held them both in his arms. The trio rocked each other gently.

I stayed in contact with Jenny and her husband for several months after. Sometimes visits consisted of a lunch, sometime just a check-in on the phone. Most visits held space for deep conversations about birth, death, and the meaning of life. Both Jenny and her husband had many thoughts on the matter, and wanted to share with someone who understood. Few of their friends or family could do so. I still remember these conversations.

In both instances, the Jennys were worried for reasons a medical professional would consider "illogical." An experienced midwife is wise to notice when a mother "overworries." She is wise to listen.

* * *

The third, and particularly puzzling stillbirth was Miriam's. She and her husband Joe were friends of friends who came to our practice for care. Miriam was a humble and kind woman who worked with the Catholic Worker Movement. She was dedicated to peace and justice, and reminded me of a saint.

I loved my visits with Miriam and Joe. She was a caring person devoted to doing good for others—her family, her friends, and her community. Joe was her soul mate, a kindred spirit. They were not the strict and dour, do-good types; on the contrary, they were joyful, engaging, and fun.

We helped Miriam through her first pregnancy, which had resulted in a difficult birth. She had acquired pre-eclampsia and was finally referred to a physician for her care. When she delivered her child slightly prematurely, she was immensely happy to have the privilege of having a healthy son. When she became pregnant again, she was filled with joy and bubbling with enthusiasm about the prospect of being a parent again. This time she hoped to give birth to a full-term infant.

I wasn't in on the birth of her second son, so I know only a few details about what went wrong. She had a long labor at home with little progress. Sometime after a transport to the hospital, where she labored a few more hours, it was decided that she should have a C-section. During preparation for surgery, they lost the baby.

When I received the phone call informing me of the news, I was devastated. I could not accept that such an injustice could happen to the kindest people I had ever known. In my memory, I had not been affected by any of the losses I had witnessed in the way I was affected by Miriam's. Doubts about my own faith, my work on births, and my life in midwifery crept in. What was the point of doing good work when tragedy could destroy it in a flash?

Yet, at her open house commemoration, Miriam not only stood steadfast, she nurtured others' grief in response to this event. Miriam and Joe invited a small group of friends and the midwives from our practice to the funeral home to say a final goodbye to their beloved son. I couldn't imagine her anguish or how she found the strength to face this fate with dignified grace and courage.

She rocked her beloved son him in her arms, and allowed each of us one by one to say our final good-byes. In that dark moment, she somehow understood that we were all in grief. She was like no other mother I have met before or after—caring for each of us in the midst of her greatest loss. I left the funeral home bewildered, wallowing in my own grief and sense of despair.

It was typical cold February day in Chicago: gray, overcast, no sun peeking through the clouds, no indication of spring. I started my car and let it heat up before pulling onto the road toward the funeral. I was empty, sad, immobilized and, for the first time ever, not wanting to do midwifery. I didn't turn on the car radio as usual, but drove in silence before feeling the impulse to sing. My alto voice found a few words to my favorite Easter hymn. I begin to sing these words, off key, unsure of their meaning, *The strife is o', the battle is won, now is the victors triumph one."*

Even now I'm still not sure why I sang that song. It just came out, bringing meaning from somewhere in my soul. I stopped when I saw the commotion in the road. Someone had struck a homeless man with a car. Never before or after had I come upon a motor vehicle accident that needed immediate attention.

In an instant, I was out of my car to assess the matter. Someone had already called the ambulance. A young girl who had been in the vehicle that hit the homeless man was cradling him in her arms, rocking him like a baby. The young man who hit him was crying and pleading for his forgiveness.

The homeless man nodded, acknowledging him. I grabbed a blanket from my car and as I approached to wrap the elderly man, he looked up at me, straight into my eyes, and I recognized God. He then looked away, closed his eyes, and took his last breath while cradled in the young girl's arms. The ambulance arrived too late.

As a modern, spiritually minded midwife, I witness the moments before birth so frequently I have come to depend on their direct reflection of God. The beautiful process of life is so perfect, I unconsciously presume it must be God's only face. Had I not witnessed the death of the homeless man, I might not have gleaned the valuable truth about the stillbirths experienced by the three women. It is this: death is equally natural, equally precious and inexplicably divine, and yet, often at conflict with human reason.

Back to Eden

What I cherish most about being a midwife is the people I meet and the relationships formed by the intimacy of the work. To be a midwife is to become a part of someone else's life. Others place their trust in my care and each of us opens our hearts. These relationships have taken me into places I would not have had the opportunity to go without being a midwife. I had the opportunity to enter homes of women of every spiritual persuasion: Catholics, Buddhist, Sufis, Muslims, and Hasidic Jews.

I remember a Saturday afternoon I spent with a Hare Krishna woman squatting in her living room as she began to deliver her infant. Her husband was at the temple and was unable to attend her birth. She spoke only Spanish and her support team spoke only English, but they communicated in chant *Hare, Hare*

Krishna," they repeated as the baby was delivered into my hands. I felt so rich for the diverse experiences my life has awarded me.

Another time, I had the honor of attending a delivery of Russian Jewish baby. The parents studied the *Kabalah* and considered themselves spiritual alternative musicians. They sat around celebrating after the birth, playing flutes and fiddles, offering me tea. I was so delighted to be invited into their lives. There is a common language to birth. Birth allows for connection.

Experiencing birth at home allows the midwife the ultimate ability to adapt herself to the surroundings of the families she serves. To enter someone's home, a midwife needs to respect the place as a sacred space where a new life will begin. She needs to have this respect, whether the home is a mansion or a basement dwelling with perhaps only a chair or two to share during a long labor. Midwives learn to adjust themselves to any setting.

One night, I remember Ceal, another midwife friend and I, went first to a birth of a wealthy woman in a huge mansion, and immediately following her birth, we found ourselves headed to another birth in a roach-infested apartment, sharing the one chair for guests, taking turns napping and guarding our bags from the roaches as the other cared for the laboring woman. We were honored to be guests at both homes and to be present at those sacred events.

Births remind us that we all enter the world naked and exposed. A woman's home carries hints of a lifetime of experience and memories. These experiences present to the midwife a more complete understanding of the many dimensions of the woman's reality.

Home can be a place of functional dwelling for external needs or a sanctuary for the soul and body. I have been privileged to visit homes of women who have mastered the ability to create a sanctuary within their homes. Their homes are healing places, where things have less meaning than the sense of being at peace, not hurried; they have become friends with the essence of being.

I remember one such home in particular. I had parked my car on a busy street. I knocked on a door of a building that appeared to be abandoned, but the address matched. On the first floor was a speak-easy coffee house. Soft jazz melted into the summer breeze from the café's dusty window as I waited for an answer to my knock.

Dan, the father, opened up the door and led me through a series of doors; original artwork painted on large canvasses lined the hallways, a few more doors, a few more stairways, led onto the roof deck. The roof was covered with a vegetable garden. There was an overstuffed sofa and used wooden chairs on the deck. Dan led me beyond this outside rooftop living room into what appeared on the outside to look like a small rooftop cottage.

We entered an urban oasis; the room had an abundance of textures of wood. It looked warm and cozy, one uninterrupted room, wooden doors and window, unpainted, many interesting old books and found objects, old vases with flowers, old comfy chairs. The city's constant background hum could not be heard. The room had several expansive skylights that enhanced the mood. Green plants and flowers were everywhere. Reused and recycled items personalized their environment. Dan was a practical man who worked with his hands.

The room was heated by an old pot-belly stove. Unused dressers drawers had become garden containers, floorboards were turned into compost bins. They grew their own vegetables, fresh herbs, made their own teas, baked their own bread, and recycled their own kitchen waste. They had little money, but had created a home in harmony with how they wanted to live their lives. Sometimes the best homes come from those with limited resources. This home provided an ideal space for birthing a child.

Jill, the mother, was laboring by candlelight. Soft Indian music played. Her long hair hung over her tan body. She spent many hours working in the community garden when she and Dan weren't attending to their underground coffee house. She felt that a home birth was congruent with her daily living practices. Key to her life was recognizing, accepting, and making peace with nature. Jill, like myself (who had two babies who were four weeks late) was overdue, but she knew that the timing of her infant's birth was in rhythm with her natural process. Overdue is a state of mind, and the illusion that we can or should control the time of birth distorts the perception of time. Too often we can rationalize a need to intervene with nature, but when we are living according to a natural state, we tend to appreciate the process. Jill's encounters with the plant world guided her understanding of her own natural processes.

When we accept the natural patterns of nature, we are rewarded by the opportunity to experience the awe and wonder of the many patterns that are revealed. This is not to say that screening and check-ups are not an important part of taking responsibility, but rather, that when we are working with healthy women, and we can identify healthy patterns, we should enhance our wisdom. It is also essential to remain humbled by how much there is to learn and revere in the nature of things. Instead of being induced at two weeks, Jill opted to wait until she naturally went into labor two weeks and two days after her due date. She felt responsible for a healthy pregnancy and in pursuing this responsibility; she could reclaim a part of herself. She was thrilled to be in labor.

Jill allowed herself to be at peace with the multisensory nature of birth; she didn't try to control her surroundings, hence the experience seemed to heighten her innate intuitive ability. She swayed with the contractions, she rested in between, a gentle summer breezed played with her hair, and she remained sitting in silence with her eyes closed. A process was taking place within her. She would moan with the contractions, her sister would lean forward with each moan, and apply pressure to her lower back. In silence, I would hand Jill a warm cloth to soothe the pain in her lower abdomen. Barb, another birth assistant, held her hand and offered Jill sips of tea and honey between contractions. Dan lay down for a nap.

In silence, we continued the process. For moments at a time, there was no wind, and the occasional dripping of a faucet could be heard. At times, we could hear Dan snoring in the background. Later, we heard the squeaks of a breast pump. Barb, a breastfeeding mother, followed her own natural rhythms and snuck off to the corner to pump her breasts for her infant at home. Jill proceeded mostly in silence, nodding to our whispers of inquiries about her desire to switch positions, go to the bathroom, and take sips of tea. The night continued at that pace.

By morning, the room was alive with sunlight. Dan had awakened and brewed a fresh pot of coffee for the team. Endorphins had allowed Jill to sleep between contractions. She was entering her own spiritual journey to dimensions that lead each woman to a place in her soul. She seemed liberated in this journey. There seemed moments where she appeared to be in complete bliss; she would smile, grin ear to ear, all with her eyes closed, and a couple contractions later, she seemed to connect to the pain and her smile would turn to a grimace, still with her eyes mostly closed.

She continued to labor calmly. Occasionally she would open her eyes, meet each of ours, smile and return to her dance, slightly moving her hips in a wide circle, which grew wider as the contractions grew in intensity.

Between the contractions, she rested her head upon her sister's shoulder. She went somewhere else. She slept and then awakened to a contraction. Again, she began her dance, her hips swirled, her feet fell into rhythm. She seemed both in control and yet out of control, something stronger than she herself was directing her labor. The contractions sent her into a trance; she let the contractions lead her in dance.

That is the essence of birth: knowing yourself better by merging with your authentic self. Jill found security in melting with all parts of herself. From the dance, she suddenly halted. She placed her hands on her knees, her head fell to her chest and her long, auburn hair hung down, covering her face. She began to push, again, in silence…until she gave a primal yell. Her head fell back, she released her jaw and relaxed her face. *"OOH-OOH-OOH,"* she moaned. Her eyes closed.

We waited as she remained at 9 cm, "with a lip," as midwives like to say. A few tricks of the trade, such as arnica and purposeful position changes, led her to complete dilation. She pushed on the birth stool, we midwives kneeling below her. After a few hours of pushing, she reached down to touch her infant's head as he crowned. The moans coaxed him out, declaring and accepting the power inside her to give birth naturally. As he birthed, she reached her down to greet him. We handed her infant up to her to hold. Her eyes wide open, her mouth agape, she was full of wonder and awe as she greeted her newborn son.

Midwifery is about guiding women through the internal and external journeys of their everyday lives. The birth of our children may be without regard to a fixed date and time; the experience of birth is the expression of eternity. Women in labor have the ability to transcend time and space, to regain a deep appreciation of the nature of their internal selves. The hormones in labor make a woman more aware of touch, smell, and taste. As these senses awaken, a woman's memories of these senses are brought forth without a particular fixed time, and often without words or thoughts. She is instead immersed in a journey of recognizing a part of her that had remained a mystery until this moment.

I often find myself also longing for balance and comfort with nature after attending to women in labor. They inspire the sides of me that I consider bad habits, like drinking too much coffee and not taking the time to eat consciously, or not spending more time outside and tending the garden. Moreover, except during births, I can forget to just "be." These habits are often driven by leading a busy life.

We long to have our internal and external dimensions integrated. In birth, this naturally unfolds. You do not need to be a spiritual scholar or have a daily practice to gain spiritual growth. A women only needs to go into the experience and the spiritual journey unfolds. Nevertheless, I have also found that women who live in harmony with nature in their daily existence can access the journey more readily.

Midwifery asks us to truly become at home with ourselves, with nature, and with women. Birth takes us out of our external experiences, our linear timing of progress, and our everyday rituals. In contrast, birth time is measured in a circular movement like the seasons. There are rhythms and patterns. If we let birth unfold with spontaneity and attuned to nature, we will end up appreciating the nature of our souls as well. For women in birth, there exists a duality of time and space. They are present both in the physical and the internal dimensions. Midwives are called to not only be medical providers, but emotional guides, allowing women to get in touch with their innermost selves, the place where the soul dwells.

About the Author

Mary Sommers is a Certified Professional Midwife (CPM) and is the Academic Director of Maternal Child Health Institute. She holds a Masters of Public Service from DePaul University. She has many years of experience and wisdom that comes from witnessing over 1,000 births in the past twenty-five years.

Early in her career, she co-founded Chicago Community Midwives, a not-for-profit home birth service. Mary has worked as a midwife, lactation consultant and doula in both Chicago, Illinois and Madison, Wisconsin. She directed several community health center's maternal child health services and nurse-midwifery programs. She is a former World Health Organization Fellow studying the maternal child health programs in Great Britain and the Netherlands. Mary is also an advisory board member of CASA, a professional midwifery school in Mexico, and a member of Compassionate Response-USA's global health partnership between Chicago and Embangweni Hospital, Malawi. She has authored educational guidebooks for doulas and midwives. Mary is the mother of five children, all born at home.

MavenMark Books is a division of HenschelHAUS Publishing.
We are happy to review manuscripts from new and veteran authors
and offer a wide range of author services,
such as coaching, editing, design, and book marketing.

Please visit www.HenschelHAUSBooks.com for submission guidelines
and our on-line bookstore.